THE BROOKLYN MUSEUM

John Singleton Copley, Mrs. William Eppes (see p. 470).

THE
BROOKLYN
MUSEUM

HANDBOOK

BROOKLYN 1967

CONTENTS

The texts were written by the following members of the staff of
The Brooklyn Museum:

Historical Introduction	*Thomas S. Buechner*
Ancient Art	*Bernard V. Bothmer*
Oriental Art	*Lois Katz*
Primitive Art	*Elizabeth Easby*
	Jane P. Rosenthal
Decorative Arts	*Dassah Saulpaugh*
	Marvin D. Schwartz
Prints and Drawings	*Una E. Johnson*
	Jo Miller
Paintings and Sculpture	*Donelson F. Hoopes*
	Arlene Jacobowitz
	Axel von Saldern

FOREWORD

When the Brooklyn Bridge supplemented the Fulton Street Ferry in 1883, people began traveling back and forth from the City of Brooklyn to the City of New York in large numbers. Today, two more bridges, a tunnel, and four subways later, the traffic is immense and in the same pattern — forth in the morning and back at night.

"This is a city of homes, containing a large proportion of quiet and intellectual people. It is free from the noise, the confusion, the distractions, and frivolities of Manhattan" wrote Augustus Healy, President of the Board of Trustees of the Brooklyn Institute of Arts and Sciences, in 1897. The Museum was created by and for Brooklynites, but the wisdom of successive governors, the generosity of discriminating benefactors in partnership with the City, and the talents of the curatorial staff have created a national treasure. Collections that would be the pride of any city in America, collections which no cultivated tourist could consider missing, exist primarily for the borough because of geographic circumstance. Such isolation has also created a community museum which serves, and is served by, a steadily increasing audience. The brief history that follows describes its evolution.

The Samuel H. Kress Foundation, with its vast experience in the visual arts, knows The Brooklyn Museum and the worthiness of its collections. The existence of this book is its gift. Those who are induced to cross the river to see the reality reflected in these pages, as well as those who want a reminder of things long loved, will share our sense of obligation to the Foundation.

THOMAS S. BUECHNER
Director

HISTORICAL INTRODUCTION

Most museums reveal what kind they are by their names: of Fine Arts, of Natural History, of the City of New York, of Glass. But The Brooklyn Museum was so named (in full) for the simple reason that it was to be a Museum of Everything for Everybody. Upon the laying of the cornerstone in 1895, Professor Hooper said: "If the Museum is wisely planned it will take into account all human history, the infinite capacity of man to act, to think, and to love . . ." Two years later at the dedication, Augustus Healy, President, described its audience by saying that none were to "be more welcome than the tired mechanic or laboring man or domestic of our household who comes to the Museum for recreation or enjoyment, or to gain a little knowledge that is elsewhere inaccessible to him of the secrets of nature or the triumphs of art."

This was no mere hyperbole on Healy's part, for as the years went by a vast variety of objects poured into the twenty-eight departments set up to receive them. Ranging from art to zoology, this institution had more diversity (and disparity) than any other in the nation. Electricity, housekeeping, political science — even psychology — were the equals of departments with tangible collections like stamps, microscopes, leaves, atlases, and paintings.

Part of the Museum was devoted to natural history, with habitat groups of stuffed animals and huge collections of eggs (4,200), moths (55,000), and sea shells (32,000). A papier-mâché squid pursued a larger-than-life octopus across the ceiling of the Hall of Invertebrates (now devoted to Egyptian art), and a mastodon skeleton failed to survive central heating in the rotunda. Terraria held the living garter snakes, frogs, and turtles which were donated each fall under parental pressure. Dr. Frederick Lucas, later director of the American Museum of Natural History, was Brooklyn's curator-in-chief when he wrote in the 1910 annual report of "our having the best exhibit of taxidermy, mimicry, and protective coloring." The devotion of the specialist is delightfully evident in another sentence from the same report: "A small but pleasing addition is the group of gila monsters."

1

Figure 1. Front Street in Brooklyn. Lithograph by G. Hayward for Henry Mc-Closkey's Manual 1865, after a painting by Francis Guy (see Plate, p.473). Augustus Graham, the Institute's first benefactor, stands on the street corner at the far left facing into this view of Brooklyn in 1820.

And the triumphs of art kept pace, with everything from plaster reproductions of Greek sculpture — the Discus Thrower, Laocoön, the Winged Victory — to fishing baskets made by the Pomo Indians of California. Curiosities and noble achievements vied for space: lace, Hindu coins, utopian views of America, chunks of mediaeval architecture, mummified Egyptian bulls, nymphs in white marble, even a Chinese cloisonné doghouse. The Brooklyn Museum was intended to contain literally everything.

The magnitude of this concept was right at home in the "City of Churches" in the 1890's. Although the Brooklyn Bridge had been open seven years, this was still an independent city whose inhabitants regarded Manhattan as a place to visit. People worked as well as lived in Brooklyn, and civic pride abounded. Manpower poured in with wave upon wave of immigrants, and with each new flood the base of the social pyramid grew. The need for education must have been beyond anything that we can imagine.

Helping to fill this need has always been the Museum's primary job. Both the need and the filling change constantly so that the history

2

of The Brooklyn Museum is the story of Brooklyn itself, first as a village, then a city, and now a borough.

1823 - 1890

The problem that sparked the creation came from too many people living in too small an area. In 1823 there were seven thousand people in the village of Brooklyn, enough to support public houses in which young men discovered the joys of liquor, of independence, and of indolence. Too sophisticated for the best-attended juvenile activity of the day, Sunday school, and not yet responsible enough to show much interest in church, they presented a very real problem. The village fathers' reaction appeared in the *Long Island Star:* "The Citizens of the Village of Brooklyn, and particularly the master mechanics, are requested to attend a meeting at the house of William Stephenson, at 8 o'clock, on Thursday (this) evening, the 7th inst, for the purpose of forming and establishing an Apprentices' Library in this village, and the reverend, the clergy, are particularly invited to attend. August 7, 1823."

A constitution was adopted, and 180 members enrolled at $ 1.75 each, payable semi-annually. Members of the board called at each door (with a wheelbarrow) to receive donations of books. By November the library was installed in a rented room at 143 Fulton Street and opened for apprentices — between 4:00 and 9:00 P.M., Saturdays only.

"To shield young men from evil associations, and to encourage improvement during leisure hours by reading and conversation" required more than five hours a week in a rented room. On the Fourth of July, 1825, General Lafayette laid the cornerstone for the Apprentice Library Association's own building at the junction of Henry and Cranberry Streets. Walt Whitman, then six years old and an eyewitness, recalled the event thirty-three years later in the *Brooklyn Daily Eagle* of June 3, 1858: "The greater part of the show consisted of the Sunday and other schools. The day was a remarkably beautiful one. The boys and girls of Brooklyn were marshalled at the old ferry, in two lines, facing inwards, with a wide space between. Lafayette came over in a carriage from New York, and passed slowly through the lines. The whole thing was old-fashioned, quiet, natural, and without cost, or at the expense of a few dollars only. After Lafayette had passed through the lines, the people who had congregated in large numbers proceeded in groups to the site of the new building. The children and some of the citizens formed a procession and marched from the ferry to the same spot. There was some delay in placing the children where they could see and hear the performances. Heaps of building materials, stone, etc., obstructed the place. Several gentlemen helped in handing the children down to stand on convenient spots in the lately excavated basement; among the rest Lafayette himself assisted. The writer well recollects the pride he felt in being one of those who happened to be taken into Lafayette's arms, and passed down."

The new building also housed the post office and police court, which suggests that the municipal administration either considered the library a basic facility or felt that such housemates would insure its success. In any case, the hours were increased from five to sixty-six per week, and girls were admitted.

Objects joined books in 1843, twenty years after the founding. Other libraries were coming into existence, schooling was improving, and Brooklyn was moving into an era of curiosity about the modern world, its inventions, its manners, and its morality. Subsistence problems were no longer primary, and the citizenry wanted to know how Brooklyn looked compared to other cities — and how it could look better. This time the problem was met by an individual benefactor, the far-sighted Augustus Graham, who moved the library to an elegant classical building on stylish Washington Street, changed the name over the door from Lyceum to Brooklyn Institute, and added an art gallery, chemical experiments, lectures, readings, concerts, and courses in drawing and French. Exhibitions included "models of machinery, curious specimens of nature and art, a fine collection of prints and flowers, a large number of pieces of sculpture, with many superior works in painting."

4

Figure 2. The Washington Street building was occupied by the Institute from 1838 until 1890 when fire destroyed it and a good part of its contents.

The Institute was the cultural life of the city of Brooklyn. Although it existed for the public, the building became a kind of headquarters for various private groups such as the Dredging Club, which dragged the floor of New York harbor for whatever might turn up. Collections of birds, shells, and fishes were maintained by other groups in a gallery with wall cases that extended all around the room from floor to ceiling. Pictures were purchased directly from the American artists Asher B. Durand, Daniel P. Huntington, and Jasper F. Cropsey, and space was rented to an art school and for artists' studios. The heart of the Institute, its noble public hall, resounded with the eloquence of such luminaries as Henry Ward Beecher and Louis Kossuth. The Institute dealt with contemporary life; collections and programs focused on what was happening then and what was to happen next.

1890-1934

In 1890 the Brooklyn Institute became the Brooklyn Institute of Arts and Sciences — a new kind of organization designed for the educational needs of a giant city bursting with power and promise. The idea of becoming all things to all people, so incredibly presumptuous in today's age of specialization, was the joyous philosophy of Professor Franklin Hooper, director of the Institute. That it was a collection of societies rather than a single building makes it almost possible to believe that the 4,244 lectures, performances, and meetings recorded for the 1900-1901 season alone actually took place. Woodrow Wilson spoke on "Bagehot the Literary Politician" and gave a course in the "Government of Cities." The principal address in 1896 was given by Booker T. Washington. Courses in art were presented by painters J. H. Twachtman and William Merritt Chase; concerts were delivered by contralto Madame Schumann-Heink, conductor Walter Damrosch, and pianist Ignace Paderewski. The range of information and ideas transmitted through lectures was limitless. Here are a few from the more than 30,000 presented between 1893 and 1913: "Housekeeper and the Garbage Question," "Remedies for Breach of Contract," "Art, a Message, and Beauty its Messenger," "Dullness and Viciousness in the Home and School," "George Sand,

Figure 3. The Museum of the Brooklyn Institute of Arts and Sciences was rendered in 1893 by A.L.V. Hoppin for the architectural firm of McKim, Mead and White.

the Emancipator of Women," "How Santa Claus Came to Simpson's Bar," "Underground Corrosion of Metals Due to Electricity Escaping from Electric Railway Lines," "Experiences of an American among the Esquimaux," and "The Clam — a Study in the Survival of the Fittest."

Professor Hooper had a building program to match. With a ten-acre plot adjacent to Prospect Park, and with McKim, Mead and White as architects, the City of Brooklyn zealously emulated New York in picking up the tab, and a most marvelous museum was conceived. An immense square, 550 feet on a side, it had three basement levels and three floors devoted to galleries. The whole building was divided in quadrants comprised of galleries surrounding glass-enclosed courtyards 100 feet square. Between these quadrants from the north door to the south door was to run the great Hall of Sculpture, interrupted by Memorial Hall in the exact center of the building, its dome rising two stories above the rest. To the east of this hall would come the Large Auditorium, to the west the Special Exhibitions Hall, both rising through three floors. The four courtyards and surrounding galleries were to contain the history of sculpture and architecture – ancient Near Eastern in one, Graeco-Roman in the second, mediaeval in the third, while all remaining categories including Renaissance, Oriental, and modern would occupy the fourth. Special emphasis was placed on huge casts of sculptures and architectural

7

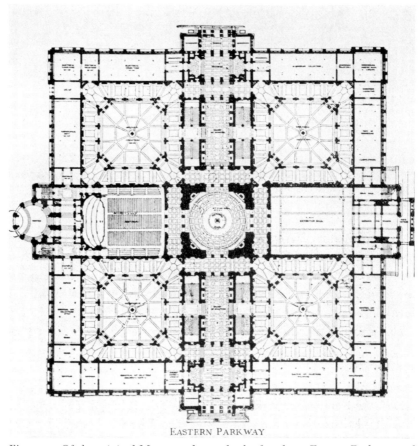

EASTERN PARKWAY

Figure 4. Of the original Museum plan, only the facade on Eastern Parkway and the north-east quadrant have been constructed.

monuments. The second floor was to contain galleries and lecture halls for the scientific and literary departments. At the west side, overlooking a no-longer-existent reservoir, the public restaurant was indicated in the form of the refectory of a mediaeval monastery. The third floor was arranged to house paintings and prints of all periods, the Music Room, and the Reference Library. A fourth floor, forming a giant cross above the Hall of Sculpture, Auditorium, and Special Exhibitions Hall, was devoted to the departments of electricity, chemistry, engineering, and music; above Memorial Hall in the center

8

Figure 5. On the Fourth of July, 1897, the first section, the west wing on Eastern Parkway, was nearing completion.

Figure 6. By 1907, the north facade and the power house behind it were completed.

Figure 7. The grand staircase, completed in 1906, was removed in 1934. During most of this period, the small door on the right side of the landing served as the main entrance.

Figure 8. All lit up for the Hudson-Fulton celebration in 1909, the Museum has its sculptures of great personages (the work supervised by Daniel Chester French) firmly in place on the architrave.

Figure 9. By 1917 the "temporary" exterior walls of the first quadrant were up, and the staff cultivated victory gardens in the space reserved for the rest.

were to be the schools of painting, sculpture, and architecture as well as the department of photography — a million and a half square feet in all, a cultural center without equal anywhere in the world.

The first section, the west wing, was opened in sight of farm land in 1897. Seven years later the central portion of the facade was completed, followed in two years by the east wing and a magnificent flight of stairs to the entrance of the central portion. Five hundred and fifty feet of north facade were finished in 1906, and the first of the four enclosed courts plus one third of the east facade were ready for installation in 1925. All was supervised and paid for by the City of Brooklyn and, after 1898, by the City of New York. The other three courts were never built, and of the million and a half square feet originally designed, a million and a quarter remain to be constructed.

Buildings have a way of taking over and running things to suit themselves. They are harder to change than words, they last longer than individuals, and they are as solid as tastes are gaseous. The

Figure 10. In 1964 Daniel Chester French's allegorical figures of Manhattan and Brooklyn, originally part of the entrance to the Manhattan Bridge, came to flank the front doors of the Museum.

miscellany brought over from the cabinets of the Washington Street building must have looked meager indeed in those hundred-foot galleries and column-ringed rotundas. The new museum had physical stature and elegance. Its proportions were noble and its embellishments refined. Like Pantagruel emerging from Gargantua, it cried to be fed in quantity and quality undreamed of.

Brooklynites had outgrown "models of machinery and curious specimens of nature and art." Their interests extended to the natural history of the whole world and to the art history of the whole past. They were consumers of information, and the purpose of the new museum was to provide it in tangible form — and by the ton. Education in art as well as in science remained the Institute's purpose, and therefore the acquisition of reproductions was emphasized. One hundred and nine full-size casts from the antique, including twenty slabs from the Parthenon Temple, were purchased for $ 2,675 in 1897. (Casts of Renaissance masterpieces came later.) This philosophy also brought in electrotypes of coins in the British Museum, fifty-seven reproductions of Arretine pottery from Boston's Museum of Fine Arts, thirty-two papier-mâché models of plants, and the awesome squid and octopus.

Photography was much respected as a major medium for bringing faraway greatness into the lives of Brooklynites. Thousands of pictures of Italian and French art and architecture, of Syria, and of geographical and natural history subjects were accumulated and displayed in quantity. One attitude characteristic of this period is summarized by the terms of a bequest received in 1903: "The interest is to be expended annually in the purchase of photographs of paintings and other works of art, plaster casts of important sculptures, and, in case the Museum is well supplied with these, of works of art."

The original concern for moral improvement ran a close second to the educational theme. As a matter of fact, when Augustus Graham endowed the Institute in 1851, $ 12,000 of the $ 27,000 that he left was to support weekly Sunday night lectures on "The Power, Wisdom, and Goodness of God as Manifested in His Works." Later the casts of Greek and Roman sculpture were particularly praised by members of the clergy as evidencing the noblest qualities of man. One of the earliest purchases of original art filled the Museum's every requirement: James Tissot's *Life of Christ* comprised 461 paintings (space filling) in excruciatingly accurate detail (very educational), painted with piety and passion (morally improving). What's more, their acquisition was urged by John Singer Sargent.

Great quantities of material were accumulated through Museum expeditions. Texas, New Mexico, California, the Queen Charlotte Islands, Japan, Egypt, France, Turkey, the Bahamas — all were visited by representatives of the departments of anthropology, archaeology, architecture, or zoology. One of the impressive collections formed as a result is that of American Southwest Indian shrines, masks, and Kachina dolls.

Identifying all these objects and subsequently arranging them in intelligible groupings was more time consuming than acquiring them. Consequently McKim, Mead and White's completed sixth of

13

Figure 11. In 1898 the Hall of Casts, including the Parthenon Frieze, occupied the third floor of the just completed west wing.

Figure 12. Some time before 1904 the paintings gallery on the fifth floor of the west wing combined patinated casts with original pictures, many of which were on loan.

14

Figure 13. By 1910, the casts of ancient sculpture, including the Parthenon Frieze, were moved from the West Gallery and set up in the Entrance Rotunda surrounding a model of the completed building.

the building has to be described in very general terms because some kind of change took place every day. The entrance to the Museum was by way of a monumental flight of steps culminating in a column-ed portico. Visitors who did not feel up to struggling to the top could

Figure 14. With the casts gone to the rotunda, the third floor of the west wing was turned over to American Indian material; in this 1911 view, a small area is devoted to the Pomo Indians of California.

duck in out of the wind at the halfway landing and enter through a narrow, damp corridor which led to the 1,300-seat lecture hall. The sturdier ones who climbed all the way to the top were rewarded, for the entrance hall was designed to evoke the noblest of sentiments. Fluted columns separated the galleries from the rotunda. Casts of antique sculptures were tastefully arrayed around a model of the completed building. To the right were displayed the fruits of Stewart Culin's expeditions in North America, embellished with a frieze of murals and plaster Indians in colorful costumes. To the left of the rotunda, antiquities, mostly Egyptian, filled cases which protruded from the wall like the teeth on a comb; beyond came the Orient and the Old World, unevenly represented by a miscellany of cloisonné, European porcelain, needlework, and English glass. The floor above, now the fourth floor, was devoted to natural history: a mastodon, eggs, and geological specimens were shown on the balcony around the rotunda, invertebrates to the east, vertebrates to the west. The top floor contained "modern art," including Renaissance casts in the center, contemporary European paintings, followed by old masters to

16

Figure 15. These white-tail deer, installed in 1915, comprised one of many habitat groups which occupied the fourth floor until natural history was abandoned in the 1930's.

the east; contemporary American painting as well as the renowned Tissot collection to the west. In small connecting galleries were installed etchings and Sargent watercolors. Stairwells contained photographs of architectural refinements, of Aztec monuments, and of the whaling industry; other odd corners were used to display laces and postage stamps.

The huge south wing, finished in 1925, brought a general rearrangement. The entrance rotunda became a Chinese Hall of State, and an entire Hindu street was set up on the first floor where the newly installed Hall of the Americas is now. Two principal additions were the costume collections and the period rooms, both European and American, on the fourth and fifth floors. The idea was to illustrate the evolution of American interiors, and between 1917 and 1929 the Museum built and furnished nineteen complete rooms. Emphasis was also placed on European decorative arts, and a Swiss

17

Figure 16. About 1933, a portion of the great hall on the first floor, now devoted to the Americas, was occupied by art from Asia, much of it on loan.

Figure 17. Although the Museum has always displayed costumes and textiles, the completion of the north-east quadrant of the building made large installations possible, such as this arrangement of 1928.

18

Figure 18. Susanna Hutchinson, Librarian and Curator of Prints, appears with Professor Goodyear in this 1914 view of the general reading room.

Gothic room, a Venetian mirrored salon, an entire full-sized Dutch house, and two halls from an Italian Renaissance palace were also assembled or recreated and installed.

The tens of thousands of objects that poured in did not come by themselves. They had to be known about, sought after, studied, acquired, installed, and preserved. The people who built the Museum, the trustees, patrons, and staff members have been legion and are as fascinating as the collections themselves. Professor William Henry Goodyear, the first curator of Fine Arts, gave various lecture courses in architecture, archaeology, and painting; one course lasted five years, with 145 different lectures. He installed hundreds of casts, devising a labeling system so prodigious in the quantity of information it contained that our present meager variety was probably born in reaction. Obviously an educator, he appears to have viewed the collections as the fruits of providence rather than policy and therefore con-

19

centrated as much on teaching aids as on art. The camera in his own hands provided exhibition after exhibition of European architectural detail. To top it all, he measured the Tower of Pisa with extraordinary care, drawing highly original conclusions about its famous inclination. Lest this summary make him appear too much of a pedant, he also acquired and installed eighty-three Sargent and twelve Homer watercolors, plus five separate collections of Egyptian material, a huge group of Chinese cloisonné, and a gorgeous array of liturgical vestments.

Stewart Culin was the ethnologist who practically filled up The Brooklyn Museum. Traveling to the Southwest, California, the Northwest, and Alaska, he shipped back the material in boxcar lots (the trustees thanked the Santa Fe Railroad in this connection in 1905 and 1906). 4,703 specimens were installed to represent the Southwest alone. He went to India, China, Korea, and Japan and built Oriental collections that included a two-story Jain rest house embellished with a hundred carved musicians who actually clanged cymbals and blew into reeds upon the turning of a crank-operated bellows. In 1920 Czechoslovakia, Hungary, and Rumania yielded hoards of costumes, textiles, and ceramics to him. A short while later he made arrangements in London, Paris, and Brussels that contributed to the collections of Oceanic and African art (1,500 objects arrived from the Belgian Congo in 1923).

Today when a special exhibition of two or three hundred pieces arrives in the Museum, all routine stops, and everyone available is assigned to its absorption. Imagine the magnitude of Culin's task in setting up thousands upon thousands of objects in meaningful installations! Imagine changing them around as wing after wing was completed! Imagine even moving the tons of immense totem poles that he acquired in Alaska. In 1908, before Culin had tapped any continent but the Americas, Dr. Lucas wrote that "instead of universal chaos there is now merely confusion." Although the situation did improve, objects acquired during expeditions frequently took years to arrive and to be installed — a Damascus room, for example, was purchased in 1913, accessioned in 1918, and installed in 1932.

Figure 19. Robert H. Rockwell, chief taxidermist from 1911 until 1922, gathering part of an Alaskan habitat group which was later set up in the Museum.

Stewart Culin wrote with the same spirit in which he collected — in quantity and with variety. The twenty-three articles that he wrote in 1926 alone ranged from anthropological research to practical tips for the garment industry. He continually applied his knowledge to the improvement of the world around him, and the Museum's famous Edward C. Blum Industrial Design Laboratory is partly the result.

1934-1966

In 1934 the monumental staircase was removed. This lack of regard for the architectural qualities of the building is a symbol of changes that began many years before. Another expression is found in the biography of Robert Rockwell, one of the Museum's hunters and taxidermists: "Modern art was beginning to show its ugly, incomprehensible forms with a vengeance and there would be no place for anything else, so I decided to look for another job." His fears were

21

well founded, and in 1931 the last animal group, the East African lions, was installed. The travel, hardship, patience, and skill necessary to secure good skins; the sculptural abilities to make them come to life; the capacity for producing the paraphernalia of natural settings, perspective distortions, and special lighting effects — all these had gone into the dozens of excellent habitat groups constructed in the Museum over the course of thirty years. Models of the unstuffable were also a specialty, the La Jolla Undersea Group being among the best. In the 1930's these were transferred to other institutions, sold, or given away, together with the moths, eggs, and geological specimens. Some, like the bear that was rendered hairless by a well-intentioned vacuum cleaning, simply fell apart. As the dust and din caused by the destruction of the stairs marked the demise of the building program, the hairless bear provided an equally dusty amen to the end of the philosophy behind it. All things to all people The Brooklyn Museum was not to be.

The Brooklyn Institute of Arts and Sciences remained the parent organization. Under the leadership of such men as Frank L. Babbott, Edward C. Blum, Adrian Van Sinderen, and their far-sighted predecessors, this change of policy was carried out to the advantage of the citizens of Brooklyn. The Children's Museum, concentrating on the sciences, made good use of many of the remaining small animal groups in its active teaching program; the Botanic Garden received the herbarium and botanic library as adjuncts to its distinguished research facilities and magnificent living collections; the Academy of Music provided more elegant and efficient spaces for lectures and the performing arts than the Museum's lost lecture hall.

On January 1, 1898, Brooklyn woke up as a borough and not a city, a borough like Queens or the Bronx, comprising many communities, all ringing Manhattan, focusing on Times Square and Grand Central Terminal. Great museums are expensive, the price of civic pride. To maintain and improve a collection of 55,000 butterflies is costly, and a collection three times as big was just a five-cent ride away in Manhattan. Besides, city streets now covered the fields and flowers that once made such insects of familiar interest. Brooklyn's taxidermy, even its papier-mâché squid, was not unique, but its Sargents and Homers were, and so were its Egyptian collections, and the period rooms from many stages of American history, and Culin's treasures from all over the world. At the same time, art was becoming a subject by itself, not simply an aid to teaching. It didn't need long labels to be enjoyed; it needed space. So The Brooklyn Museum became an art museum — gradually and certainly. It remained an educational institution, but the emphasis shifted from giving out information to demonstrating quality.

From the very beginning, the lion's share of acquisition funds had gone to art and ethnology, and a great many fine objects were acquired before the entrance was brought down to earth. The job for the curators in the 'thirties was to weed out and reinstall, and to collect as well as limited means would allow. The ultimate goal was the aesthetic encounter, a kind of mystical conversation between the object of art and the viewer.

Good fortune smiled. In 1931 The Brooklyn Museum found itself with a large annual income restricted to the purchase of Egyptian art, more than any other institution in the world had for that purpose. It came, indirectly, from Charles Edwin Wilbour, who, having made a fortune in the printing business in New York City, retired and went abroad. In 1882, after a delightful season in Paris, he found Egypt even more satisfactory to his means and scholarly disposition. For fourteen years he plied the Nile in a luxurious boat built for the purpose; on board "The Seven Hathors," every important Egyptologist of the day enjoyed his hospitality. In 1916, twenty years after his death, the Charles Edwin Wilbour Collection came to the Museum. Except for a handful of fine pieces, it was large but undistinguished. Of real importance, however, was the acquisition of his library, notes, and papers. He had purchased literally everything in print about Egypt and had written his mother weekly, cataloguing in detail the historic archaeological events which were taking place. The endowment came in 1931 with the death of his only son, Victor — and the interest on it has built one of the finest collections of Egyptian art in the world. An additional gift arrived in 1947 in a big steamer trunk from a warehouse in Newark. Wrapped in newspapers of the 'eighties and 'nineties was the greatest "find" of Egyptian papyri of modern times. In addition to texts in hieratic and demotic, it comprised the largest body of Biblical Aramaic in America: the correspondence of a Jewish military colony at Elephantine Island in the fifth century B.C.

The story of the Wilbour Fund is a cynic's delight. All the Museum's devotion to policy and program, all these treasured threads of continuity stretching back to 1823, have little to do with the fact that Egyptian art is one of Brooklyn's great strengths. A collection of no great interest, turned down by The Metropolitan Museum of Art, found its way to Brooklyn, to be followed fifteen years later by a great deal of money from a son whose final will honored the memory of his father. The memorial thus created grows in stature as each new acquisition is presented to the public in the name of Charles Edwin Wilbour.

In terms of most of its patrons, however, the growth of the collection is surprisingly orderly. Strength in the arts of the Americas from pre-Columbian Mexico to contemporary printmakers is not accidental. The patriotic predilection of the board in 1855 is evident in its purchase of Jasper Cropsey's painting of Niagara Falls, and the expanding interest in things American is reflected a century later in the loans and gifts of major pre-Columbian objects from the collections of board members Ernest Erickson and Alastair Bradley Martin. Today's superb American paintings collection was built over a long period of time, Eakins by Eakins, Homer after Homer, with enviable moments for the purchase in bunches of Sargents, Innesses, and Ryders. The gradual accumulation by purchase of the best collection of Peruvian textiles outside of Peru was a matter of policy, as is the concentration on American decorative arts. Unlike the Wilbour Fund, the Lever Fund received in 1964 came because H. Randolph Lever wanted to help the Museum improve something that it already had — the American period rooms.

It seems unfair not to describe in detail the generosities of the Babbotts, Underwoods, Havemeyers, Friedsams, Putnams, Ramsays, Pratts, Kevorkians, and many others, for they have enabled the Mu-

24

Figure 20. The gallery now devoted to late Egyptian art on the third floor of the west wing was successively occupied by antique casts, Indians of North America and, in 1928, by Invertebrates.

25

seum to devote itself to art with the essential emphasis on quality. It is characteristic of the present that individual benefactors should share the credit for the Museum's development with such foundations as Avalon, Ford, Kress, and New York. Curiously, foundations are no less individual in their likes and dislikes than private patrons and, therefore, the Museum continues to grow in a somewhat haphazard manner, doing splendidly with the primitive arts of the Americas, for example, but having no money at all to improve its Oriental collections.

As the acquisitive character of the Museum evolves, the program of activities changes accordingly. One robin's egg is pretty much like another, and a person who has a piece of copper ore in New York can live without seeing another in Philadelphia. Not so with art. As nature's accomplishments gave way to man's, The Brooklyn Museum became both borrower and lender. The idea of a granite warehouse of erudition, with comprehensive exhibits explaining everything for eternity, was gradually superseded by burlap-covered walls (nail holes do not show) playing host to an endless stream of fortnightly guests. In 1933, for example, a special exhibition opened on the average of every eleven days. Although the joys of the aesthetic wallop were widely experienced, nobody really knew what caused them (nobody still does), so that these assemblages of things pleasant to look at were always packaged according to some aesthetically irrelevant common characteristic and wrapped up in educational string: "Masks, Egypt to Gas" (1941), "Here's How" (1953; drinking vessels), "What Cortez Found in Mexico" (1948), and so forth. The special-exhibition format brought the world closer than the photographs of architectural details and plaster casts of famous sculptures had been able to do. Whatever the device, original work of almost every period and place has visited Brooklyn — from "Egyptian Sculpture of the Late Period" to "Turner Watercolors from the British Museum."

This borough has had as many kinds of people in it as Ellis Island. A living museum of ethnology itself, Brooklyn has always provided reasons and audiences cosmopolitan for exhibitions — from the "Swedish National Art Exhibition" of 1916 to "The Negro Artist Comes

26

Figure 21. Art of France, a special exhibition in 1918, occupied the elegant central rotunda on the fifth floor, since "modernized" into a sculpture court.

of Age" in 1946. One series, begun already twenty years ago and now repeated every two years, has become a national institution: The Brooklyn Museum's Print Biennial — what's new and what's best in the graphic arts of America.

The educational function remained but its form changed radically in the 'thirties. Plaster casts were neglected because they were considered uninspiring. This was part of the same turning point marked by the demolition of the stairs. The collections had been assembled almost entirely for teaching purposes (conveying moral as well as historic truths). In the new era, this aspect was split off and directed largely towards children. Objects had to be original and, in the eyes of the times, beautiful. An extensive and successful Education Department resulted which continues to expose hundreds of thousands of children to every cultural area imaginable, including con-

Figure 22. The inspirational atmosphere generated by the works of art in the gallery of European painting on the fifth floor is utilized by a sketch class, this one in 1924.

Figure 23. Public school teachers continue to attend special classes in the Museum as they did in the early 1920's when this photograph was made.

Figure 24. In 1932, pupils of Ruth St. Denis posed about the fountain in the Auditorium Court, then used primarily for sculpture.

Figure 25. Indians from the Southwest demonstrated various crafts in the Auditorium Court as part of the educational program of 1932.

Figure 26. In 1949, Max Beckmann was an instructor at The Brooklyn Museum Art School.

certs on the evolution of musical instruments, painting classes, and demonstrations in all sorts of creative techniques.

Objects were often treated with embarrassing reverence during the first decade of the Museum's total concentration on art. Long empty walls, painted white so that a picture or two could breathe, had a way of making everything look precious, foreign, and as if it needed

Figure 27. In this photograph taken in 1950, Hanna T. Rose, Curator of Education, is talking to a group of children dressed in costumes from the study collection.

cleaning. Labels were thought to confuse the view, and information was considered a hindrance to aesthetic enjoyment. The visitor entered a space so subtle in its proportions, so empty, so colorless that he was immediately reduced to a state of tranquillity bordering on the insensible.

The job for that generation was to get everything out of the way so that the work of art could exercise its mystical magnetism. The job for this generation is to make everything available so that today's better-educated visitor can select what he needs or wants for himself. This means making art as accessible and familiar as is consistent with proper care and preservation; allowing designers, fashion students, and manufacturers to work directly with the collections, as in the Edward C. Blum Design Laboratory; selling folk art from all over the world in the Gallery Shop, so that remote and exotic things can be seen, touched, and owned by everybody; enabling ladies from

31

Figure 28. The Museum's Gallery Shop sells original folk art from sixty-five countries and, before Christmas, is the most popular of all departments.

the Museum's Community Committee to carry the cultures of Japan, India, or Mexico to schools and hospitals through the "Museum on Wheels" program.

Selling, lending, giving, and storing were essential activities of the space-consuming 'thirties. In the 'sixties visitors know more, care more, and want more. As much of the Museum's collection as possible ought to be visible. One manifestation of this conviction is the Hall of the Americas, a 280,000-cubic-foot space restored to McKim, Mead and White grandeur. Four giant cases, each twenty-eight feet square, reveal the Museum's almost incredible wealth in Mayan and Aztec sculpture, Peruvian textiles, stone carvings from Costa Rica, Kachina dolls from New Mexico, and wood carvings from the Northwest coast. Installed in cases big enough for people, objects are arranged, lighted, and even animated to suggest their function in a life-size scale. Another example of maximum availability is the new Paintings Study Gallery on the fifth floor. Eliminating storerooms, this one space holds more than a thousand pictures. Sky-lit with supplementary artificial lighting, each picture is visible in a permanent place on a sliding or rotating panel. The visitor can look up an artist or period in the location file and, literally, have access to our entire holdings.

Today the quantities that Americans consume require ever more efficient mass production. Extruding, spinning, stamping, and pouring, the great machinery of our civilization eliminates the hand of man, eliminates any trace of an individual personality shaping an individual product. As a result, the individual products of the past are becoming increasingly rare — and important. This melancholy fact was the motivation for the Museum's Frieda Schiff Warburg Memorial Sculpture Garden, consisting of architectural ornament saved from New York buildings torn down in recent years. In less than a single lifetime the grimacing face on a tenement keystone has changed from a fussy superfluity to a fascinating creation. During the same period a life-size terracotta figure of an Etruscan warrior changed from a work of art of colossal magnitude to a proven forgery. These are profound reminders of the fallibility of taste, both public and professional. Connoisseurship must continue to separate the better from the best, and primary galleries should always contain the pick of the collections. But the rest must come out of hiding.

In addition to the Paintings Study Gallery, similar halls are planned so that the storerooms of all departments can be emptied into the light of public scrutiny. In the case of costumes, for example, motor-driven conveyors will deliver Worth gowns, peasant embroideries, and the haute couture of the recent past before glass windows — at the press of a button. Prints in plastic sandwiches on sliding tracks will be available in the hundreds. The whole vast complex of the decorative arts — metals, ceramics, glass, and textiles — will provide a three-dimensional dictionary of American craftsmanship.

Figure 29.   One of forty-eight sections comprising the Hall of the Americas, completed in 1965.

No one yet knows all the knowledge or all the stimulus that any object is capable of — but a huge amount is known. The problem is what should be transmitted and how. Professor Goodyear's labels of a generation ago may have been a bore and worse: they may have so cluttered up the view as to detract from the object. But the man who did not know what to do in front of a plaster pietà could at least read. This Museum still feels obliged to provide all its visitors with reasons to look, to provide other points of view, and to suggest the context in which the object was created.

We are trying to fill these responsibilities in various ways, from labels to study tours traveling literally all over the world. Our new labels are audible as well as visible and will bring the voice of an artist talking about his own picture, the sound of a Cherokee ceremony, or the song of a Persian poet. The visitor will be able to examine the household inventory of a seventeenth-century American, see aerial views of the Moundbuilder's mounds in Ohio, or read the admonitions of an Egyptian father to his son written 5,000 years ago.

Figure 30. The Paintings Study Gallery contains 984 pictures with space for another 300. The entire reserve collection of American and European paintings and watercolors was made accessible in 1967.

Over the past four years we have taken almost 400 Museum Members on study tours — up the Nile to Abu Simbel, to Machu Picchu high in the Andes, to the Greek Islands, and around the Golden Horn. Supervised by Mrs. Earle Kress Williams and conducted by scholars from other museums as well as the Brooklyn, these include lectures prior to departure and unique opportunities to visit sites, excavations, collections, and officials not generally accessible to travelers. The insight into our own collections which such study affords is profound.

Museums serve three masters, and all require constant attention. The general public loves objects, their manner of presentation, and constant replacement. The collection loves stable atmospheric conditions, cleanliness, and protection from the public. And scholarship loves total access, complex facilities, and endless time, so that each

35

Figure 31. Four Atlantes are among the hundreds of architectural ornaments preserved in the Frieda Schiff Warburg Memorial Sculpture Garden, completed in 1966.

work of art can increase in power as our knowledge about it grows. All three focus on the best things that men have made. Some of Brooklyn's best are illustrated in the following pages.

Ancient Art

Bird Deity

From Mohamerieh, near Edfu
Painted pottery
Museum Collection Fund

Early Predynastic Period,
about 4000 B. C.
H. $11^7/_{16}$ in. (29.5 cm)
07.447.505

The first art practiced by man in the ancient Nile Valley was sculpture in the round, and this figure of a female with uplifted arms and a bird's head represents man's earliest attempt to picture tangibly a religious concept, namely that of the spirit of the dead.

Such bird-headed spirits occur in the early religion of many civilizations, always endowed with a human body but with arms raised like wings and with the face of a bird. This figure came to light in a tomb of one of the earliest prehistoric cultures of ancient Egypt, the so-called Amratian Period. It was found in the course of an excavation undertaken on behalf of The Brooklyn Museum by the French scholar Henri de Morgan. Stylized and yet true to nature the statuette reflects an artistic taste of great sophistication.

40

Tripod Vessel

From Mohamcrieh, near Edfu
Red-polished pottery with white design
Museum Collection Fund

Early Predynastic Period,
about 4000 B. C.
H. 6¼ in. (15.9 cm)
07.447.399

At the end of the fifth millennium B. C., when the people of the northern Nile Valley developed a culture which distinguished them from other people of northeast Africa, they entered the last phase of prehistoric existence, which we call the Predynastic Period.

From the beginning of their Predynastic civilization the Egyptians showed a high degree of imagination in the decoration of pottery, both in color and design. They also developed fairly rapidly a great variety of shapes; later the forms of pottery became much simpler. This tripod vessel represents a very rare type: its red-polished surface bears a design in white which combines man-made elements, the matting, and patterns found in nature, the plant stems.

Vase with Animal Decoration

From Aulad Yahya, near Akhmim
Buff pottery with red painting
Charles Edwin Wilbour Fund

Late Predynastic Period,
about 3200 B. C.
H. 12^9/$_{16}$ in. (32 cm)
61.87

The Egyptians, with their innate feeling for color and decoration, produced, strangely enough, painted pottery in only two periods of their long history: from about 4000 to 3200 B. C., and from 1420 to 1300 B. C. This vessel dates from the earlier of the two, at the end of Predynastic times, when a free and easy style of painting was briefly adopted in the decoration of a small group of tall vessels of which less than a dozen examples are known today. No two of them show identical motifs, and yet their characteristics are unmistakable: a procession of animals often interrupted by linear decorations of much elegance.

The upper portion of the Brooklyn vase shows a number of aardvarks, clumsy burrowing animals which no longer exist in Egypt. Although the wiggly lines on the lower part of the vessel may represent snakes, they must be considered primarily a decorative base for the amusing troop that ambles above.

42

43

Knife of a Hunter

From Abu Zeidan, south of Edfu
Flint and ivory
Museum Collection Fund

Early Dynastic Period,
about 3100 B. C.
Length 9⅛ in. (23.2 cm)
09.889.118

The two finest stone knives from ancient Egypt with decorated ivory handles are in the Musée du Louvre and in this Museum. The Louvre piece was acquired in the antiquities market in Cairo; the Brooklyn knife was found in a controlled excavation with the entire contents of its owner's tomb.

The graceful ripples caused by chipping the flint blade are not uncommon, but the rich decoration of the handle demands attention because so little relief decoration has survived from Predynastic times. Numerous rows of animals have been carved with minute care and great delicacy on both sides, and although their arrangement in row upon row is rather formal, it presages the ordered discipline of later Egyptian wall representations. They embody in all probability the fulfillment of what was hoped for by the man in whose tomb the knife had been deposited: an abundance of game to be hunted forever in the hereafter.

The boss is pierced lengthwise, providing a hole through which presumably a string or leather thong was passed so as to secure the weapon to the bearer's wrist.

Colossal Head of a King

Red granite
Charles Edwin Wilbour Fund

Early Dynastic Period,
end of Dynasty III,
about 2600 B. C.
H. 21⅜ in. (54.3 cm)
46.167

Since the beginning of the historical period (about 3150 B. C.) political life of ancient Egypt focused on divine kingship; all activities of the country revolved to a degree hard to define today around the person of the ruler. This position of a god on earth was maintained by Pharaoh for nearly three thousand years, but as society in the Nile Valley grew more complex, the idea of kingship, its concept, and its religious significance were gradually modified.

The earliest representations of Egyptian kings are on a small scale. Not until Dynasty III were statues made which show the ruler life-size; this forceful head wearing the tall crown of Upper Egypt even surpasses human scale, both in measurements and in its aim to depict the godlike power and strength of the Pharaoh.

The style of the head suggests the period just prior to the rise of Dynasty IV; it is the only one of its kind in hard stone remaining from this period. Its archaic character is underlined by the simplicity of the features which, in their almost brutal directness, are devoid of the kind of sophistication which marks Egyptian statuary of later periods.

Inspection of Cattle

From Saqqarah

Limestone

Charles Edwin Wilbour Fund

Old Kingdom, Dynasty V,

about 2420 B. C.

H. 20^1/$_{16}$ in. (51 cm)

49.62

Egyptian art can be divided technically into two main fields: one is three-dimensional, and the other two-dimensional. The first consists of sculpture in the round, the latter of relief and painting. Relief work is a kind of modified drawing, either standing out on the background or sunken into the background. The first is called raised relief, the second sunk relief. Here we have a fine example of low raised relief of the Old Kingdom.

Relief work was employed to decorate the temples of the kings and gods of ancient Egypt as well as the tombs of private persons. The decoration consists of ornaments, inscriptions, and especially of representations reflecting the religious beliefs of the dwellers of the Nile Valley and depicting in faithful detail their daily life.

Two servants wearing kilts and an unclad herdsman have brought four heads of prize cattle, to be either inspected or slaughtered. The longhorn breed is neatly labeled by the two hieroglyphs over the animals' backs which spell the name of the species, "yuwa." The inscription on the right belongs to a long column of text, the beginning and end of which have been lost; it seems to refer to a series of holy places.

49

Methethy as a Mature Man

From Saqqarah
Wood, covered with gesso and painted
Charles Edwin Wilbour Fund

Old Kingdom,
early Dynasty VI,
about 2340 B.C.
H. 24³/₁₆ in. (61.5 cm)
Height of head
4⅝ in. (11.7 cm)
51.1

In the collection of The Brooklyn Museum are three statues of an
estate administrator named Methethy. The one illustrated is the finest
of them, primarily because it shows features far surpassing the idealizing expression which characterizes most Egyptian sculpture. It is
the highly individual representation of the face of a sophisticated and
intelligent official of ancient Egypt; there is no duplicate and no
copy to be found of this figure which indeed approaches true portraiture.

50

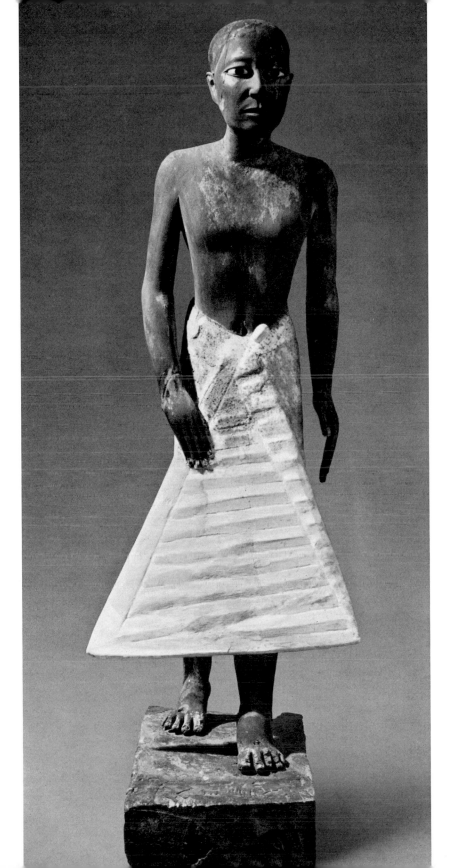

In spite of the perishable material the statue is well preserved; the remarkable elements which make for the highly lifelike expression of the face, namely the eyes, are still in place in spite of the fact that they were inlaid with stones within a copper frame and inserted into the sockets ages ago. Their calm gaze endows the face with a human quality that brings the person represented close to the observer and imparts an expression of Methethy's personality, more than four thousand years after this extraordinary likeness was created.

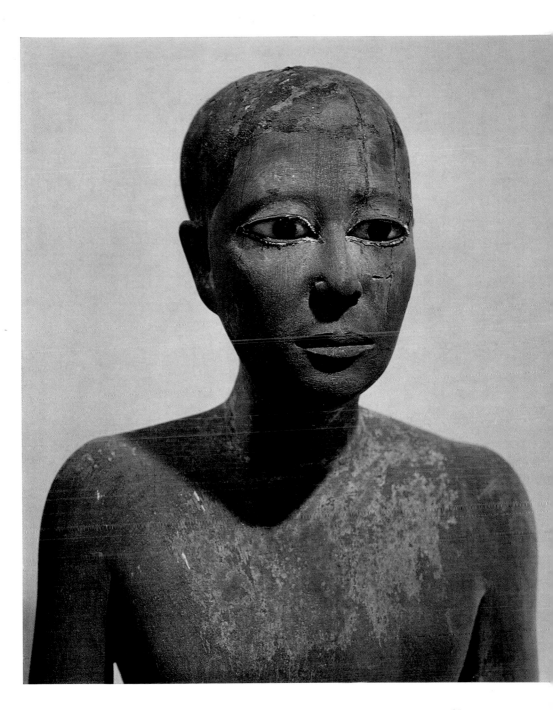

King Pepy II with his Mother

Perhaps from Saqqarah

Alabaster

Charles Edwin Wilbour Fund

Old Kingdom, Dynasty VI,

about 2230 B. C.

H. 15^7/$_{16}$ in. (39.2 cm)

39.119

There is no inscribed royal statuary from Dynasty VI preserved, except for three sculptures in this Museum. One represents King Pepy I in a kneeling attitude, the second shows him seated; by far the most interesting of the group is this statue of Queen Ankhnes-mery-ra holding her son, King Pepy II, on her lap. The sculpture is carved from a single piece of alabaster; the technique is unusual inasmuch as the limbs are for the most part freely modeled in the round instead of being connected to the main mass of the statue by means of "bridges" which were meant to prevent breakage.

The two figures are each strictly frontal, without direct relationship to one another. The composition featuring the large-scale mother with the small-scale boy-king on her lap represents an important departure from the traditional and apparently constitutes an attempt to enrich the repertoire of the statuary. No such group sculpture had ever been made before, and it was to take more than eight hundred years before anything similar was attempted again by an Egyptian artist.

Queen and Hairdresser

From Deir el Bahri (Thebes)
Limestone, with traces of paint
Charles Edwin Wilbour Fund

Early Middle Kingdom,
Dynasty XI,
about 2030 B.C.
H. 7½ in (19 cm)
54.49

In raised relief (see p. 48) the background is cut away and the representation left standing; in sunk relief the representation is "sunk" into the background which is left untouched. In the brilliant light of Egypt, sunk relief has a far more dramatic effect than low, raised relief; this is probably one of the reasons why it was employed with increasing frequency in the course of Egyptian history.

The crisp, bold style of this relief is typical of the new beginning, which was made at Thebes a century or more after the Old Kingdom had collapsed at the end of Dynasty VI. The fragment came from the underground tomb chamber of Queen Neferu (one of the wives of King Menthu-hotep II), which was carved out of the bedrock below the King's funerary temple at western Thebes.

The Queen is attended by her faithful hairdresser, Henut, who attaches an artificial braid to her mistress' coiffure. Another lock is pinned up with a bodkin to be held out of the way until the new braid has been put into place. The features of queen and handmaiden are almost identical because they do not represent the individuals named, but reflect the then prevailing ideal female face as carved in the court studios of Menthu-hotep II at Thebes. The prominent nose, the strong indication of the nostril, full lips, and a slanting, highly stylized ear mark unmistakably the characteristic way of cutting relief in the latter part of the reign of this King.

57

Female Bust

Black mottled granite
Charles Edwin Wilbour Fund

Middle Kingdom,
early Dynasty XII,
about 1950-1900 B.C.
H. 9⁵/₁₆ in. (23.6 cm)
59.1

There is no way of telling who this lady was because the sculpture is
devoid of inscription, and the simple costume merely indicates that
she was a private person and not of royal rank. With its open,
friendly features the face exudes human warmth as well as a positive
attitude toward the unknown deity in whose temple the statue was
once dedicated. It speaks well for the equality of the sexes in ancient
Egypt that a private lady could have a sculpture made for herself.

The heavy tripartite wig frames the broad face and passes behind
the ears, thus giving the impression of forcing them forward. They
are large in keeping with the ancient Egyptian ideal of beauty; the
same ideal required small breasts, and also in this respect the sculpture is no exception. Whereas the natural curve of the eyebrows dips
toward the root of the nose, the artificial eyebrows in low relief are
absolutely straight above the inner corners of the eyes, a feature
which places the bust early in Dynasty XII. Around 1900 B.C. these
artificial eyebrows, too, began to follow the natural curve and dipped
down toward the nose.

58

King Sesostris III

From Hierakonpolis
Black granite
Charles Edwin Wilbour Fund

Middle Kingdom,
Dynasty XII,
1878-1843 B.C.
H. 21½ in. (54.5 cm)
52.1

The sculpture represents Sesostris III, a ruler who left a lasting mark
on the history of Egyptian art because he was the first pharaoh of the
Nile Valley who had his features modeled in a realistic, rather than
idealizing, fashion. Whereas his predecessors, since the early Old
Kingdom, were mainly shown with forceful, yet youthful traits, his
face is careworn and hard and distinctly shows the signs of age. It is
framed by the striped headcloth, the *nemes*, which once bore an
uraeus, the royal cobra, above the forehead. In contrast to the en-
ergetic, almost brutal features of the face, the torso is rendered in an
idealizing manner.

   The dominating majesty of an Egyptian pharaoh, who had a statue
of himself presented to his god in a sanctuary or temple, is reflected
in this dynamic figure which, although seated and looking straight
ahead, is full of nervous energy and vibrant strength. There is no
humility in the attitude of Sesostris III when facing his god as in this
sculpture. A long and wearisome life has left a mark on the King's
features which he proudly displays like a badge of honor in the presence of the deity.

Squatting Man

Quartzite
Charles Edwin Wilbour Fund

Middle Kingdom,
late Dynasty XII
or early Dynasty XIII,
about 1790-1750 B.C.
H. 27½ in. (69.8 cm)
62.77.1

With supreme calm this ancient Egyptian nobleman is squatting on the ground, prepared to face his god in the hereafter. He has a cloak wrapped about himself; his left hand rests on his chest in a gesture of devotion.

The broad face, with heavy-lidded eyes and worry lines descending from the corners of the mouth, conveys the impression of a complex personality — quite in contrast to the simplicity of the head-cloth and the highly stylized ears and left hand. This obvious simplicity attracts the observer to the face, and it is most likely that this was done intentionally. The brooding mood of the eyes, the pensive expression, and the almost disdainful mouth seem to characterize the owner better than any outer trappings or even an inscription, although it must be noted that a brief offering formula was once written on top of the base in front of the legs.

Yet it is impossible to identify this man because these same brooding and sorrowful features occur in several other sculptures from the end of Dynasty XII and the beginning of Dynasty XIII; one can therefore assume that these faces constitute a characteristic type of the period, rather than representing the individual features of definite persons.

King Amenhotep III

Diorite
Charles Edwin Wilbour Fund

New Kingdom,
Dynasty XVIII,
about 1415 B. C.
H. 24⅜ in. (61.9 cm)
59.19

This King has been likened to Louis XIV of France because of his splendid court life, his predilection for worldly pleasures, and his unstinting support of the arts which in his time reflected the supreme refinement of royal taste.

When this colossal head was made, probably as part of a coronation statue now lost, the King had just ascended to the throne and may have been no more than twelve or thirteen years old. There is something boyish and yet highly sophisticated in these features which, with the sweeping eyebrows and slanting eyes, were to set a new style of male representation, widely imitated among his courtiers and followers up and down the Nile Valley.

In spite of the vastly over-lifesize scale of the head its features are graceful and elegant. The noble simplicity of the early New Kingdom had long disappeared. Instead, the style changed markedly and became far richer and more varied than ever before — probably thanks to the great influence this King exercised in the decoration of his temples and palaces.

64

65

Lady Thepu

Thebes, Tomb no. 181
Painting on gesso over mud plaster
Charles Edwin Wilbour Fund

New Kingdom,
Dynasty XVIII,
reign of Amenhotep III,
about 1400 B. C.
H. of figure 11⅞ in.
(30.2 cm)
65.197

The art of painting was practiced in all great periods of Egyptian art, from the Predynastic age to Roman times. In Dynasty XVIII, it achieved its greatest height, particularly during the reigns of Tuthmosis IV and Amenhotep III. The fragmentary panel of the Lady Thepu dates from the time of the latter king.

She is a well-known personality who appears in several inscriptions and mural paintings in the tomb which her son, the Chief Sculptor Nebamun, shared with another sculptor, probably his predecessor. The woman is dressed in the finery of the great ladies of her time, with a perfumed ointment cone on her heavy wig, the forehead decorated with a diadem, a polychrome collar around her neck, a white shift, and a diaphanous shawl over her shoulders which leaves one breast bare.

The stars over the lady's raised hand are the remains of three columns of text now mostly lost, ending with her name of which the three last signs are still preserved behind the wig. Although a mature woman by the time the mural was painted, she is represented in the glory of eternal youth in keeping with the idealizing style of the time.

66

Princess Meket-aten

Probably from Tell el Amarna
Brown quartzite
Charles Edwin Wilbour Collection

New Kingdom,
Dynasty XVIII,
Amarna Period,
about 1370 B. C.
H. 11¼ in. (28.5 cm)
16.46

When Charles Edwin Wilbour acquired this fragmentary sculpture at Akhmim in Middle Egypt in 1890, he was told it had been found at Tell el Amarna, the capital of Akhenaten's spiritual kingdom of the Living Sun Disk, the Aten. This provenance is very likely to be correct because the girl whose name appears on the back pillar was the second daughter of King Akhenaten and Queen Nofretity, a princess known to have died at Amarna. The moving scene of mourning for the girl by her parents, as depicted in the royal tomb, is justly famous.

Although today devoid of the head and of most of the limbs, this torso in light brown stone retains much of the lovely figure of the young princess. Her right arm was hanging by her side; the left crosses over below her breasts, and the missing hand probably held a pet bird.

Royal Couple

From Tell el Amarna
Limestone, with traces of paint
Charles Edwin Wilbour Collection

New Kingdom,
Dynasty XVIII,
Amarna Period,
about 1360 B.C.
H. 6³/₁₆ in. (15.7 cm)
16.48

After the sophistication and elegance which mark the style of the reign of King Amenhotep III, a startling change took place early in the reign of his son, Amenhotep IV, who assumed the name of Akhenaten. This new style was highly naturalistic, even realistic in comparison with that of the time of his father, and at the same time the traditional repertoire of subject matter was greatly enlarged.

Akhenaten founded a new capital in honor of his god, Aten, and it was here that Charles Edwin Wilbour acquired this relief on December 22, 1881.

The slab shows the heads of a young royal couple in sunk relief, a king on the left with his queen on the right; for a long time they had been identified as Akhenaten and his consort Nofretity. But all known representations of the famous King depict him with features far more drawn and less youthful. Although the pharaoh shown here slightly resembles Akhenaten, he is undoubtedly a youth and thus must be Akhenaten's son-in-law and successor, King Semenkh-ka-ra.

The same holds true for the head of the queen who, although she wears a cap first encountered in representations of the famous Nofretity, resembles her very little apart from a vague family likeness. Semenkh-ka-ra indeed married Nofretity's daughter, Merit-aten, and it is she who is here most probably represented with her young husband.

70

Bust of a Nobleman

Painted limestone
Charles Edwin Wilbour Fund

New Kingdom,
Dynasties XIX-XX,
about 1250-1200 B. C.
H. 20½ in. (52 cm)
36.261

The dry elegance of this formal representation of a great official belongs to the Ramesside Period, at the close of the New Kingdom. Despite the splendor of coiffure and garment, the figure represents a man. Carved in sunk relief, the abundance of detail is confined to his attire; the face, far more summarily executed, dominates through the fine delineation of its contour. A few generations later a marked decline set in, and even the faces of kings and noblemen are devoid of all expression; this lasted through the Third Intermediate Period, Dynasties XXI-XXIV (about 1100-720 B. C.).

The scene to which this relief once belonged showed the man probably in the act of offering before the gods. He was followed by his wife or another female member of his household because a hand holds a sistrum, or rattle, which was only used by women in religious processions and other ceremonies.

Openwork Vase

From Upper Egypt
Blue frit
Charles Edwin Wilbour Fund

Third Intermediate Period,
Dynasties XXI-XXII,
about 1000-800 B. C.
H. $6^{11}/_{16}$ in. (17 cm)
44.175

This famous vase, one of the finest made of this material in ancient Egypt, was once in the MacGregor Collection, but there is no indication where its first owner of record acquired it. First shown at an exhibition of Egyptian art at Burlington House in London in 1895, it has been illustrated several times since as the most elaborate vessel ever made in the long history of ancient Egyptian glassmaking. It was molded of frit, powdered glass that had been made into a paste by adding water, and then fired at a low temperature so that the material became solid without turning into true glass.

The ovoid body of the bottle has a bottom in the form of a lotus flower which is surmounted by deities and mythological symbols. The neck opens into a mouth decorated as a lotus blossom: an elegant crowning, yet so simple in contrast to the fancy work of the vessel's body.

King Osorkon I

From Shibin el Qanatir, near Heliopolis
Bronze, solid cast, with gold inlays
Charles Edwin Wilbour Fund

Third Intermediate Period,
Dynasty XXII,
915-900 B.C.
H. 5½ in. (14 cm)
57.92

The Third Intermediate Period constitutes a time of transition between the age of Egypt's greatest political power, the New Kingdom,
and the revival during the Late Period, in the wake of the domination
by Egypt's Kushite neighbors to the south. Some of the elegance of
the New Kingdom survived, but on the whole sculpture was not produced in profusion, probably because the centralized power of great
kingship was lacking in Egpyt for several hundred years.

It is at this time that bronze, well-known to the Egyptians for
hundreds of years, came more and more into use. They vastly improved on the foreign technique of casting metal sculptures by
perfecting inlay work with gold threads such as is found in this
statuette of King Osorkon I. The inscriptions, the pattern of the royal
kilt, and the figures of the gods which circle the torso of the pharaoh
were all created by cutting into the metal with a sharp instrument,
embedding into the groove a gold thread, and then hammering the
slightly raised surface down so as to be even with the surrounding
area.

Head of Thoëris

Hematite
Charles Edwin Wilbour Fund

Third Intermediate Period,
Dynasties XXI-XXV,
about 1000-700 B.C.
H. $^{15}/_{16}$ in. (2.4 cm)
58.92

The dark and shiny surface of this monster's head reflects the moist element in which the Nile hippopotamus dwells. But this is not a hippo plain and simple; it is the mighty Thoëris, mistress of childbirth and protectress against snakebite and other evil household hazards, who, in the guise of a pregnant hippopotamus with sagging breasts and crocodile's teeth, inspired awe and good will in the women of ancient Egypt.

In the figure now lost she was shown striding, with long strands of hair falling over her shoulders, her ample belly barely supported by short, bandy lion's legs, and her semi-human arms resting on the hieroglyph denoting protection. She is an ugly creature indeed, and yet the crispness of the carving in the extremely hard metallic stone invites detailed observation which in turn arouses admiration from the modern amateur as it must have from the ancient believer.

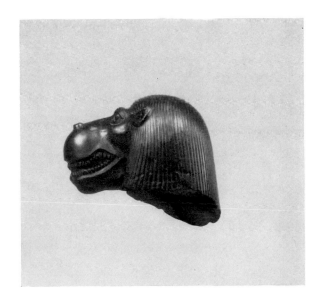

Assur-nasir-pal II, King of Assyria

From Nimrud, Iraq

Alabaster

Gift of Hagop Kevorkian

Assyria, about 880 B.C.

H. 7 feet 7⅛ in. (2.315 m)

55.155

The twelve large alabaster slabs from the north-west palace of the Assyrian King Assur-nasir-pal II (883-859 B.C.) at Nimrud form an important section of the Middle Eastern collection of this Museum. The foremost set of such reliefs in this country, they were removed to London in 1853 and two years later brought to Boston where they were acquired by Mr. James Lenox. He presented them to the New-York Historical Society in 1858; in 1937 they were lent to The Brooklyn Museum which in 1955 became the owner through the generosity of the late Mr. Kevorkian.

Here the King is shown in procession, holding on his raised hand a vessel of precious metal and in the other hand a bow. His hair and beard are carefully groomed; a long pendant — probably of gold — adorns his ear, and the haft of a dagger protrudes from under his garment. A long inscription in cuneiform writing extends across the middle of the slab, covering both the King's figure and that of his companion, a winged genius or deity whose raised hand bears an unusual detail, the natural lines of the palm.

82

Persian Guard

From the Apadana at Persepolis
Grey limestone
Gift of The Kevorkian Foundation

Persia, about 500 B.C.,
reign of Darius I
H. 10¼ in. (26.1 cm)
65.195

The soldier, bearing a shield and once carrying a spear, is one of a long file of royal guards that marched solemnly across a parapet of the audience hall in the palace at Persepolis. This fragment probably comes from the center of the west face of the parapet bordering the central landing.

Appropriately, these guardians decorated the landing of the Apadana (audience hall), embodying the nobility and strength of the *Ten Thousand Immortals*, the cream of the Achaemenid army, which conquered the lands bordering the Eastern Mediterranean. While other members of this corps are shown with bow and quiver as well as the lance, all wore their hair in uniformly curled locks, under the *cidaris*, the tall fluted headgear, and were dressed in long flowing robes.

This kind of low relief was much favored by the Persians and, although based on an Assyrian prototype, could hardly have been executed on such a vast scale by Achaemenid workmen. Ionian Greek and even Egyptian craftsmen may have helped, which accounts for some of the sophistication in these representations reflecting an international rather than provincial Persian style.

Lion Vessel

Probably from Leontopolis, Lower Egypt   Late Period,
Alabaster   Dynasty XXVII,
Charles Edwin Wilbour Fund   525-404 B. C.
H. $4^3/_{16}$ in. (10.6 cm)
53.223

With the first period of Persian domination, from the late sixth to the fifth century B. C., numerous artistic and political accomplishments of the ancient Middle East were brought to Egypt by the conquering Achaemenids. Although Egyptian statuary was not directly affected, costumes and ornaments employed by the Persians were frequently adapted to native taste by Egyptian artisans. A good example is the little lion, here shown holding an ointment vessel, with numerous cutout depressions carved in his skin — a form of surface ornamentation which hitherto had been foreign to Egyptian art. These cutouts once held polychrome inlays which must have enhanced the yellow-and-white alabaster to startling effect.

One of a small group of lions holding vessels, all found in the Delta, this little figure was most likely used in a temple ritual. Its place of origin presumably was a great temple dedicated to the Egyptian deity Mahes, a lion god much venerated by the Persians when they came to the Nile Valley.

Ibex Handle

From Tell el Maskhuta, Eastern Delta
Silver
Charles Edwin Wilbour Fund

Late Dynasty XXVII,
about 410 B.C.
H. 6⁹/₁₆ in. (16.7 cm)
54.50.41

Near the site of Biblical Pithom, in the Land of Goshen, mercenaries of north Semitic origin served as frontier guards when the Persians dominated Egypt from 525 to 404 B.C. There was a temple on the site dedicated to the Semitic goddess Alat, and from the treasure of its sanctuary the Museum has a set of fine silver vessels and ornaments in gold and semiprecious stones which combine Achaemenid and Egyptian elements.

The handle of one of these vessels is fashioned in the shape of a jumping ibex with forelegs folded under and the hind legs extended along the stem of the handle. Although Persian in style this piece probably was made locally by an Egyptian artisan since it so obviously reflects the solidity of Egyptian sculpture rather than the lithe elegance of Achaemenid workmanship of the fifth century B.C.

86

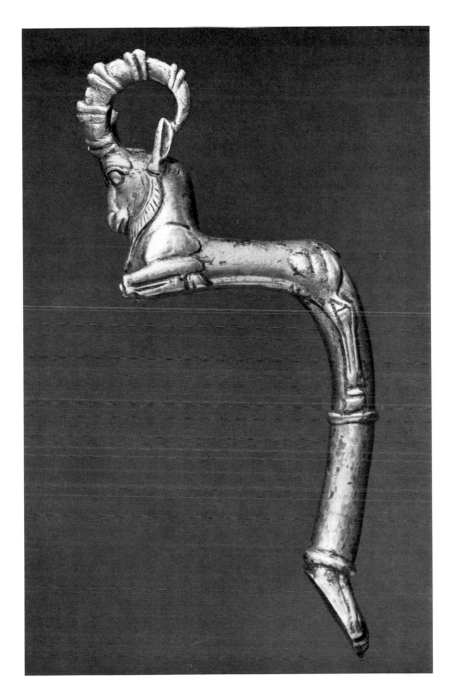

Wesir-wer's Head

From Karnak
Green schist (metamorphic slate)
Charles Edwin Wilbour Fund

Late Period,
Dynasty XXX,
about 360 B. C.
H. 5⅞ in. (15 cm)
55.175

Wesir-wer was Chief of the Prophets of the God Monthu at Thebes. The head of his statue has been in The Brooklyn Museum for more than ten years whereas the body was discovered about sixty years ago at the Temple of Amun in Karnak, at Thebes, and has been in the Cairo Museum ever since.

This is probably the best individual likeness sculptured in Egypt in the fourth century B. C. and undoubtedly was modeled from life. The unwrinkled mask of skin, stretched tightly over the bone structure, presents a face of great intelligence and — especially around the mouth — determination. Made a generation before Alexander the Great conquered Egypt in 332 B. C., the head shows not the slightest trace of Greek influence. On the contrary, it presents a classic example of the archaistic tendencies for which Dynasty XXX is well known. Simplicity in the structure of the face and sparing means employed in modeling the features are characteristic of this period. As the best example of this type of portraiture, the head of Wesir-wer stands stylistically about midway between the realistic likenesses of the early Persian Period and the greatest portrait of the Ptolemaic Period, the "Green Head" in Boston.

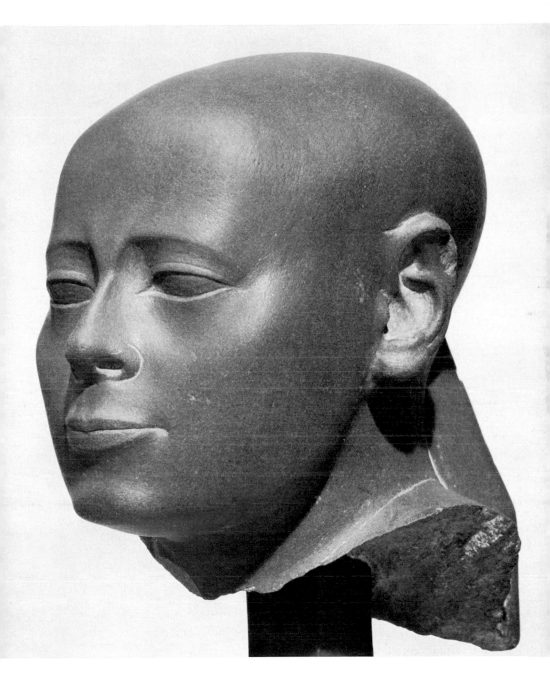

King and Goddess

Basalt
Charles Edwin Wilbour Fund

Ptolemaic Period,
3rd century B. C.
H. 7¾ in. (19.7 cm)
62.46

Here is a scene of two figures of equal height and equal importance, a goddess on the left and a king on the right, surmounted by the star-studded hieroglyph meaning "sky." The slim figure of the deity has a caption which calls her "Hathor, Mistress of the Southern Sycamore Tree," a sacred tree known to have been venerated at Memphis since the third millennium B. C.

In thousands of years the image of the goddess had not changed: she was still pictured as the beautiful female, wearing a crown of cow horns with the sun disk on her head. The king, who is presenting her with two ritual rattles, is probably Ptolemy II (285-246 B. C.). In the column of inscription below his hands he addresses her as his mother, and she in turn, in the text below her outstretched arm holding the scepter, promises him divine "endowment."

The purpose of the relief is somewhat of a puzzle; it could hardly have been an ex-voto since the edges would not have been left in the rough. Thus one can only surmise that it formed part of the decoration of a shrine covered with numerous similar scenes of king and deity which was broken up before it had been completed. The workmanship is unusually careful and finely executed, considering the small scale and the hardness of the material.

90

91

Alexander the Great

Egyptian alabaster
Charles Edwin Wilbour Fund

Hellenistic,
2nd century B.C.
H. $3^9/16$ in. (9 cm)
54.162

Around the middle of the fourth century B.C. a young Greek king from Macedonia, Alexander, soon to be called the Great, consolidated the Greek states under his leadership and went on to conquer most of the Middle East. He thus extended the influence of Hellenic civilization far into Africa and Asia. In Egypt he founded the city which still bears his name and which, within a century, became one of the great centers of Hellenistic culture.

While he was still alive Alexander was already worshiped as a god, and his likeness in stone and metal was widely distributed throughout his empire. Long after his death fine portraits of the youthful and vigorous hero continued to be produced throughout the Hellenistic world.

This portrait bust in Alexandrian style may have been combined with other materials to form a complete figure. Attachment holes around the head indicate that it wore a crown or diadem, probably of gold. The intense upward gaze, the luxuriant hair, and the emotional expression of the mouth are characteristic of the later, idealized representations that have kept alive the memory of Alexander the Great, of his exploits and vivid personality.

92

Head of Sarapis

Glassy faience
Charles Edwin Wilbour Fund

Alexandrian,
1st century A.D.
H. 4 in. (10.1 cm)
58.79.1

When the Ptolemies, the successors to Alexander the Great, assumed government of the Greek communities in Egypt, they established an official god who combined both Greek and Egyptian qualities in order to appeal to native Egyptians as well as to the Greek settlers. The god, Sarapis, had properties of Osiris, Egyptian god of the underworld, and of the bull Apis, his earthly incarnation, while many of his powers and characteristics were identified with Zeus and the healer Asklepios. As the cult spread through the Eastern Mediterranean, Sarapis cult shrines were frequently related to Isis sanctuaries; under the Empire, they extended throughout the entire Roman world.

The luxuriant beard and hair are characteristic of Sarapis — especially the locks springing up from the center of the forehead. Behind the front rows of curls is a broad flat band, and on top of the head is a roughly circular broken place that was probably the base of an attribute. In the case of Sarapis, it would have been either bovine horns, or a *modius* or basket-shaped corn measure appropriate to the fertility aspects of the god.

95

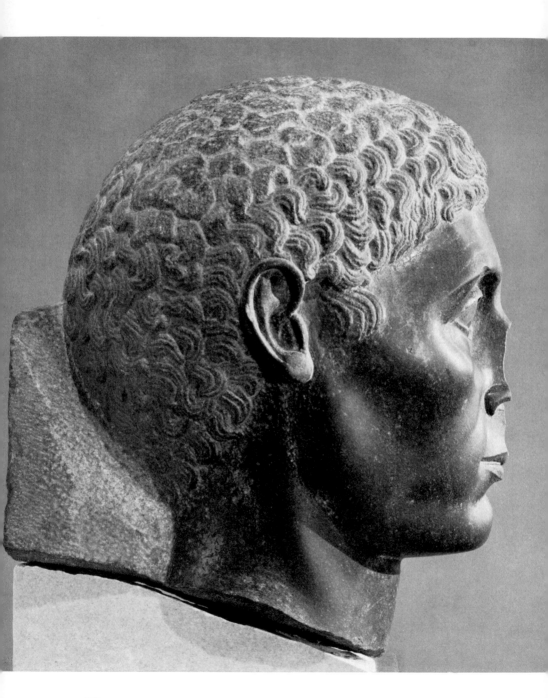

The "Brooklyn Black Head"

From Mitrahineh (Memphis)
Black diorite
Charles Edwin Wilbour Fund

Late Ptolemaic Period,
about 80 B. C.
H. 16¼ in. (41.4 cm)
58.30

Among the great Egyptian portraits of the Late Period, the "Brooklyn Black Head" represents a sculpture with both Egyptian and Hellenistic elements. The heroic scale, the strict frontality, and the inscription on the back pillar are in the pharaonic tradition; whereas the curly hair, the wide open eyes, and the high degree of asymmetry of the features are due to Greek influence.

This is a portrait in the best sense of the word. It does not represent a type, but the modeling seems to follow faithfully the individual features of a definite person, rendering both the physical likeness and something of the quality of his inner personality.

The man immortalized in the "Brooklyn Black Head," though anonymous at present, was undoubtedly a high-ranking official, possibly even the Governor of Memphis in the declining years of Ptolemaic rule. Stylistically the sculpture is datable to about 80 B. C., and thus the portrayed may well have served Ptolemy XII, father of Cleopatra VII, or even the eminent Queen herself.

98

Trained Bear

From Egypt
Bronze
Charles Edwin Wilbour Fund

Roman,
1st-2nd century A.D.
H. 3⅛ in. (9.8 cm)
58.97

With his forepaws raised, the squat little bear seems to have just sat down after performing a dance at the urging of his trainer. Such scenes are not unknown on the streets of Near Eastern cities even in modern times.

The leafy, wreath-like collar masks the joint of the "lid," which is the top of the head from the upper jaws, with a hinge at the back of the neck. With the lid raised, the benign beast appears more to be yawning than roaring. Two loops at the lower edge of the collar and under the ears were probably used for fastening the lid or suspending the vessel by cords. The receptacle may have been a container for liquid pigment or perfume, for medicine or even for bear fat that was used in ancient times in cosmetics and pharmacology.

Boy of Isis Cult

From El Rubiyat, Fayoum
Tempera on cypress wood panel
Charles Edwin Wilbour Fund

Coptic Period,
about A. D. 300-350
H. 11¾ in. (30.2 cm)
41.848

The practice of incorporating an image of the human face into mummy coverings reaches far back into earliest Egyptian burial customs. Modeled in plaster or in cartonnage and later painted on flat, wooden panels wrapped over the mummy's face, these portraits represent the deceased in variously stylized or realistic fashions. The large eyes and the direct and solemn mien of this youth are extensions of the tradition of earlier mummy masks.

The young boy in this painting is an acolyte of the Isis cult. He grasps a cup and a garland as emblems of his religious belief and wears the side hairlock long associated with the child-god Horus. Worship of Isis, sister and consort of Osiris and mother of Horus, was modified as it was assimilated by the Greeks and later by the Romans when they occupied Egypt. Often associated with the worship of Serapis, Isis cults spread throughout the Mediterranean countries and persisted well into the sixth century A. D.

Woman with Cross

From Sheikh Ibada (Antinoöpolis),   Coptic Period,
Upper Egypt   4th century A.D.
Limestone   H. 14 in. (35.6 cm)
Charles Edwin Wilbour Fund   63.36

The Coptic Period of Egypt comprises the centuries of declining Graeco-Roman and rising Christian civilizations in the Nile Valley; its art employed both Hellenistic-Roman subjects and Christian motifs. Human figures with identifiable Christian symbols such as the cross are unusual.

The open face and large eyes characterize the simple, direct manner of representation which is typical of Coptic art. Since it expresses the sentiments of the native lower and middle classes, and not those of the Romans who administered Egypt at that time, it lacks sophistication and reflects a kind of naive provincialism which is also found in the architecture and literature of the Copts.

The strict frontality in the pose of the lady is, of course, a feature directly derived from ancient Egyptian statuary. In spite of the stylistic link with an old artistic tradition, the purpose and meaning of the statue are not at all clear. It may represent a saint or martyr or perhaps a worshipful lady who donated an image of herself to her parish church or to a sanctuary to which she made a pilgrimage.

The One Cured of Paralysis

From Sheikh Ibada (Antinoöpolis), Coptic Period,
Upper Egypt about A.D. 400
Limestone, with traces of polychromy H. 24¼ in. (61.5 cm)
Charles Edwin Wilbour Fund 62.44

This statue, representing a man who is rising to carry his bed, is one of the few examples in Coptic art which illustrates a Biblical subject in sculpture in the round on a large scale. The figure is that of the Paralytic whose miraculous cure is related in the New Testament (Matthew 9:6, Mark 2:3, Luke 5:11) when he was told by Christ: "Arise, and take up thy bed, and go into thine house."

The fact that he is shown naked is unusual because the subject occurs occasionally in early Christian art where the Paralytic invariably is dressed in a simple tunic with a cord around his waist. But Upper Egypt, where this sculpture was created, is distant from the centers of early Christian iconography, and thus the subject of the Paralytic's body — the physical appearance of the sick now cured — has been approached in a somewhat primitive manner.

104

Menorah

From Hammam Lif, Tunisia	3rd to 5th century A.D.
Stone mosaic	H. 22⅝ in. (57.4 cm)
Museum Collection Fund	W. 34¹⁵/₁₆ in. (88.8 cm)
	05.26

In 1883, in the main sanctuary of a synagogue in a Tunisian town, a French army officer discovered a mosaic pavement composed of several sections. Twenty parts of this pavement were taken to Paris and thence, in 1905, brought to this Museum. It has been possible to piece together the general composition of the entire mosaic from the sections in the Museum and from the sketches made by the soldier who found them, in spite of the fact that the whereabouts of many fragments are unknown.

Representing a variety of natural creatures, plants, and symbolic objects, these mosaics are constructed in *opus tessellatum*, or stone cubes of fairly equal size set in a cement binder. The palette is muted, restricted to the colors of natural stones.

The seven-branched candlestick, the menorah, became in Roman times one of the predominant symbols of Judaism. It is incorporated into several ancient Jewish mosaics in buildings in Palestine and other sites bordering the Eastern and Southern Mediterranean. Here, it is shown in simplified, almost schematic form, set in a circle within a lozenge from which tendrils sprout.

107

Pitcher with Marine Decoration

From Egypt

Buff-colored terracotta

Abbott Collection,

Charles Edwin Wilbour Fund

Minoan-Mycenaean,

1500-1425 B. C.

H. 8^{11}/$_{16}$ in. (22 cm)

37.13 E

Around the Aegean Sea a number of pre-Hellenic civilizations had become prominent since the Bronze Age. On Crete, the Minoans led an apparently peaceful and prosperous existence that thrived on their sea-girt island; so attractive was this way of life that the mainland Mycenaeans moved in from the Peloponnesus. That contacts between the island inhabitants and their neighbors in the Eastern Mediterranean were wide-spread is attested to by the fact that this jug was found in Egypt.

Minoan knowledge of the sea was continued by the Mycenaeans in their frequent use of marine forms among the many natural motifs employed in the decoration of beautifully designed utilitarian and decorative objects. The four large creatures on this spouted pitcher are nautiluses (sometimes called argonauts) which jauntily wave their tentacles in a rhythmic if unrealistic fashion. Corals, algae, and other sea life fill every space in an underwater composition bursting with vitality.

109

Amphora with the Death of Orpheus

From Vulci, Italy
Red-figured pottery
Museum Collection Fund

Attic, about 470 B.C.,
attributed to the Niobid Painter
H. with cover $20^{15}/_{16}$ in. (53.2 cm)
59.34

Amphorae were used for many centuries in Greece and throughout
the Mediterranean world for storage and transportation of liquid and
solid provisions. This ovoid shape with a distinct joining between
body and neck of the vessel is called a neck-amphora and was often
covered with a lid, wheel-made as was the vase itself. The red-figure
painting technique, introduced in the latter part of the sixth century
B.C., leaves the figures the red color of the fired clay and covers the
background with shiny black glaze.

Orpheus, the consummate musician, is traditionally connected with Thrace, in northern Greece. His musical artistry charmed all living things but was also, perhaps indirectly, the cause of his death. According to one tradition, the women of Trace, angered by their husbands' attention to Orpheus' cult, tore him limb from limb. It is these women who are represented by the lady brandishing a household spit to attack the musician as he sits in the rocky landscape.

Oriental Art

Jar

Iran, Kashan (?) ware
White painted in black on
relief decoration, overall
blue glaze
Gift of Horace Havemeyer

13th century A.D.
H. 12¾ in. (32.3 cm)
42.212.41

From the ninth to the fourteenth century Islamic pottery reached great heights. Impetus came from the demand for fine pottery created by familiarity with imported Chinese stoneware and porcelain. In Iran in the eleventh or twelfth century a revolutionary change took place in the manufacture of ceramics. Instead of using lead glazes over natural clays potters began to employ alkaline glazes over a new, almost pure, white body composed of quartz and small quantities of ash and clay. At first painting under the alkaline glaze presented difficulties similar to those encountered earlier with lead glazes: colors tended to run and smudge the design when the glaze melted. Potters, therefore, reverted to a technique used earlier with lead glazes — making a pigment stable by mixing it with a thick paste of clay slip.

Alkaline-glazed ware of some refinement, as exemplified by this jar, was made chiefly in Kashan. The vessels always have a band of Kufic inscription on a foliated background, and many feature a band of fish decorating the neck.

117

Bahram Gur in a Peasant's House

Iran, Shiraz

Watercolor on paper

Ella C. Woodward Memorial Fund

About A.D. 1325

Page: 6⁵/₁₆ by 5¹¹/₁₆ in.

(16 by 14.5 cm)

36.239

Miniature painting which primarily embellished poems and chronicles became a dominant art form in the Islamic world in the twelfth and early thirteenth centuries. The artists, working predominantly in guilds, mostly followed the movements of the royal courts from capital to capital.

In the early fourteenth century, a new style of painting, centering in Shiraz, appeared in Iran. The Shiraz school produced a number of *Shah-Namah* (Book of Kings), written by the poet Firdausi (A.D. 940-1030), which contained the first major cycle of illuminations. The miniature illustrated here is from a dispersed book generally referred to as the "second small Shah-Namah." It illustrates the passage of the poem that relates an incident involving King Bahram Gur in a peasant's house to which he had withdrawn. Bahram has heard the peasant's wife complain about the corruption of the court and about the Shah who does not take better care of his country's affairs. Offended, he decides to become a tyrant and rule severely. The next morning, when the woman attempted to milk her cow, it refused to give milk. She complained to her husband that this only occurred when the Shah has become unjust and tyrannous. Hearing this, Bahram repented and promised to be a just ruler.

118

بخش بالایی (راست به چپ):

ستون ۱ (راست):
زهر چند محم اندر ایکر آب
بساخت هرچه بستد بلبگی
ستنگم رشت شهر یا اگر شاه
جو کام کرد رون بهانه بود
بیگشت اندرون کار کرد مرد
چراکه باز کاو کمتر بود
بیزینجمن از کهن کیک کار
بام جاو ندرد کشت

ستون ۲:
کورن بوشم زانکه آداب
بام خواهندی بارویخت
دشت و سرخ بسی رست اندرها
زکردن روز نهان بادسیاه
خدمت کورداری خرد
هم اینجور رنشت بر بود
نواز دارنده روزگار
که بیروز نگاری بهان ازن

ستون ۳:
توارک رهرگان آستان ظهر
دلاک زنکشای از زرویز
خیرکز دزل کی سی افزارسی
نهان نهاد اندرون زمانه شک
شده نمایه درزرعانات شاه
کهادزهاه باران برد مبع
دکوکه شدنگ شاه ازاو
ارزبر ما خنجه شاهی همیناد
هم مرزبان کهنت نشین

ستون ۴:
وراز کشتی ازاره پرویز
بفال زنده اندروز زیاننگ
بستان منرابی بارون شعرک
بستان بر خشک کنت شیر
اکباب کرداز مزداد
هفت

ستون ۵:
شاندکی سندوراز آداب
باخم خواوندی بارویخت
جو ازاده کرش بهان آذرشاه
بیگشت اندرون کار کرد مرد
چراکه باز کاو کمتر بود
بیزینجمن از کهن کیک کار
بام جاو ندرد کشت

پایین تصویر (راست به چپ):

ستون ۱:
که بادرا رای شاه ازها
ومردار ازنار زبرد دیت
خیرکز بیتر زرنای نکرد
همی معزبارنانه دکاه
بصراه را ورگ بیت مرا
دوازدیوان زبانه بریت شاه
همرازساه مارا بربن پشنگ
بریوزتر ما ابرازنان مکن
ترکی بگیر زمانه بریوم
ببمرازدرون مزناربا نهفت
ربروشن ملک شکری کرد
ترازی درمیزرزیاباد بوم
برابیشم سیکا و شور انگج

ستون ۲:
بیجا داراری شاهی بره دیت
خیرکز بیتر زرنای مرد
همی معزبارنانه دکاه
خدا و نظامنه سوشن بخت
بازه حمد عنش شیبان
که شاه ماعز کزداجخت
کهجوزا وشنبر خانه همان
کفتارابیباره مرزیای

ستون ۳:
کهبرماحمدندوزجار زازرس
میریدنوان ازنست کرزخلا
باوبخا کیباشدکزر
همی داشنازاره مازبکیکام
برزی مثوی کنناره مرخار شاه
نهان جاه ندرون زنبی ورا
بوکفتن صرام کای رفیه
برزی کهکنجدکشتی نجوزم
برزجم رادمار بارن سری

ستون ۴:
نهاده برکوکه کی شاخ بردانه
نلکه برکوکه کی شاخ بردلمنه
بریادمانه ادار نی مساه
جمرم در هردور عالا شاه
ربدفواشوی بالزرانتا
نزاداده امروز و ابرویم
نوزم وهکو به ده شکانکج
کسی رادکتی نزدگکی
خواندهمی اشهبازبرا
هلوانی بر ستاره شکروم
کهربس مردن برجم آنین

ستون ۵:
نهمی ازاران لشرکشه مول
جه دریا بدی وبی ودریا
باماکیبه ارادماه برکنت
بیزنامل دکاه زاده ی رسانه
حنرمرزیهره در دور کهات
ربدفواشوی بالزرای
نزاده امروز و ابرویم
نوزم وهکو به ده شکانکج
خواندهمی اشهبازبرا
همکوراه ی لشرکروم
کهنوهلوانی و برسرابنت
نزادل بیاری مزرم آندر

پانل تزئینی (عنوان):
برون آمدن گشتاسپ از توران و رفتن نزد کتایون

Hunters in Landscape

by Riza-i-Abbasi (active A. D. 1603-1635) About A. D. 1615
Iran, Isfahan, Shah Abbas School 8½ by 5¼ in.
Brush drawing with color and (20.7 by 13.3 cm)
gold on polished paper 35.1027
Museum Collection Fund

In 1598, Isfahan became the capital of Shah-Abbas I (1587-1629) and the center of a new painting style which radiated to other parts of Iran. Its chief characteristic, an almost calligraphic refinement of line combined with lightness and elegance of brushwork, derived from the first great school of Persian drawing centered earlier at Qazwin.

One of the great artists associated with the Isfahan school was Riza-i-Abbasi whose technical ability in handling the brush was unsurpassed. This drawing, only lightly tinted, is executed in the typical manner of the Isfahan Court school. Risa-i-Abbasi, while continuing the style for which the school was famous, introduced a new palette of colors based on shades of purple and brown. What distinguishes his work, however, is its pure design which verges on the abstract and emphasizes the expressive quality of lines.

Fragment of a Carpet

Northern Iran, Tabirz
White cotton warps and wefts,
sehna knots
Presented in memory of
Florence Gibb Pratt

About A.D. 1550
65 by 39⅜ in.
(165 by 100 cm)
36.213 a-g

Iranian rugs of the Safavid period (1502-1736), and Turkish and Caucasian rugs of the Ottoman period (1517-1914) have become well known outside the Islamic world by the ubiquitous, although not always accurate, term "Persian rugs." Its use is no doubt due to the fact that the true "Persian" (Iranian) rugs are of great variety both in design and color and served as models for types produced in Turkey, India, the Caucasus, and other centers of manufacture. This fragment was one of seven pieces which were originally part of two or more sixteenth-century "Persian" wool-pile carpets.

Iranian rugs of the fifteenth and sixteenth centuries are very rare. Extant examples show a preference for brilliantly colored medallion designs (eight or sixteen-pointed stars) and naturalistically treated floral and animal patterns. The medallion motif was especially popular in book bindings and ornamental pages, usually surrounded by delicate floral scrolls. In some of the rugs winged female figures are depicted as seen in the fragment illustrated here. These are probably houris, the beautiful maidens who, according to Islamic belief, attend the blessed in paradise.

Tara

India, Orissa
Stone
Carll H. De Silver and
Ella C. Woodward Funds

8th century A.D.
H. 106³/₁₆ in. (271.2 cm)
60.138

Buddhism, a powerful religion in India from the third century B.C. onward, exercised an enormous influence throughout eastern Asia. Evolved first in the fifth century as a reforming and evangelical faith in opposition to early Hinduism, it developed eventually into a complex ritualistic system. An increased interest in the Hindu practice of magico-religious rites, and the Hindu concept of Sakti as the female energy of a god, led to the creation of the "Tantric System" which appeared in organized Buddhism about the seventh century A.D.

The goddess Tara who helps to cross the ocean of existence, is an example of the adoption of the Sakti concept as the female energy of a Bodhisattva. The image illustrated here represents one of the many forms the goddess may take. Below, to her right, is a worshipper. On her left appears to be a four-armed Ekajatâ, frequently the left-sided attendant of the green Tara. Two of the arms carry a lasso and an elephant goad, the other two arms retain the same position as those in her larger version.

Siva Nataraja

South India   12th-13th century A.D.
Bronze   H. 30 in. (76.2 cm)
Gift of Frank L. Babbott   27.959

Hinduism is the name for the native religion and social system of India. Although essentially monotheistic, Hindus assigned, for convenience and for simplifying worship, the attributes or powers of the godhead individually to three main gods: Brahma, the Creator; Vishnu, the Preserver; and Siva, the Destroyer, each of whom may manifest himself in other forms according to need.

Siva, as Nataraja, is Lord of the Dance; an elaborate iconography accompanies him. The dancing position he takes symbolizes his eternal activity of creating and destroying everything in the world.

According to legend, Siva performed this dance after he had overcome a tiger, a serpent, and a malignant dwarf; the tiger skin he is wearing, the cobras wrapped around his arms, and the dwarf he is crushing, recall his victory. In addition, the drum he holds in one of his right hands stands for the primordial sound, the flame in one of his left hands, for destruction. His raised right hand gestures "Fear not," and his other free hand points to his foot to indicate the refuge of the soul. In his forehead is the third eye of spiritual wisdom. The crescent moon and the Ganges River, in form of a mermaid, are set in his hair: when the gods decided to send the goddess Ganga (the Ganges River) to earth for the good of men, Siva sacrificed himself by taking the goddess down upon his topknot and acting as buffer for her fall.

127

Zummurad Shah in his Tent

India, Agra   A.D. 1567-1587
Opaque watercolor and gold on cotton   36⅞ by 29½ in.
Museum Collection Fund   (93.8 by 75 cm)
                                               24.49

Mughal painting in India was produced for the Muslim emperors of the Mughal Dynasty (1526-1857), their courtiers and provincial governors. Mainly an aristocratic court art it introduced, for the first time in India, entirely secular subject matters which were chiefly concerned with portraying individuals or interpreting historical events. The Hamzah-Namah, a Persian romance of unknown authorship, is the largest and most extraordinary of Mughal Indian tales and illustrates the semi-apocryphal adventures of Amir Hamzah. Born at Mecca about A.D. 569, he was the uncle of Mohammad, founder of the Islamic faith.

In 1567, the Mughal emperor Akbar, for whom the story of Hamzah was a particular favorite, commissioned a vast illustrated copy of it to be made. Abu'l Fazl, Akbar's historian, records in the Statutes of Akbar that "the story of Hamzah was represented in twelve (unsewn) volumes, and clever painters made the most astonishing illustrations for no less than 1400 passages." The paintings were probably the work of many artists and bear close relation to Iranian miniature painting. This scene, one of four miniatures from the Hamzah-Namah belonging to the Museum, illustrates an episode from the third section of the romance which deals with Amir Hamzah's battles with the giant, Zummurad Shah.

The Concert

India, Rajasthan School
Watercolor on paper
A. Augustus Healy and
Frank L. Babbott Funds

Second half of the
17th century A. D.
$14^{11}/_{16}$ by $11^7/_{16}$ in.
(38 by 29 cm)
36.253

The history of miniature painting in India is more complicated than in the Islamic world. Miniatures were produced by, and for, the followers of four different religious traditions — Buddhists, Jains, Hindus, and Muslims — and they are divided into two major categories, Mughal and Rajput. An example of Mughal painting is seen in the preceding illustration. Rajput painting flourished in Rajasthan ("abode of the princes") and in several hill states of the Punjab well into the nineteenth century. Primarily Hindu, one of its main themes were Ragamala, poems describing musical modes which were represented in human form: the Ragas or "Princes," and the sub-modes, their Raginis or "ladies."

This miniature depicts the Bilawal Ragini and expresses the mood felt by a lady who is about to meet her lover. The Bilawal Ragini is a melody which should be sung in the morning, and it is possible that the musicians in this picture are playing and singing this music while the heroine completes the sixteen items of her toilette. Feelings of expectation and joy are evident not only in the serious intentness of all participants, but also find expression in the passionate vermilion of the heroine's room and the vessels of beauty preparation standing ready to serve while outside the peacocks, symbols of love and luxury, are shrieking.

Curtain

India, Golconda or northern Madras   A.D. 1630-1640
Painting on cotton   108½ by 37¾ in.
Museum Collection Fund   (275 by 96 cm)
                                      14.719.2

This painted cotton is one of seven panels originally belonging to a single curtain supposedly from the Amber Palace in Jaipur, India. The hanging is associated with a group of cotton paintings possibly executed in the kingdom of Golconda during the seventeenth century. The curtain was originally twenty-three feet wide and eight feet high. Its painted face, representing people in, or known to, India, was so fragile when acquired by the Museum that it was cut into seven sections, and each panel was separately mounted on canvas.

The craftsmen who executed the paintings worked from stencil plates made of paper on which outlines of the pattern were traced with ink and perforated with holes. The stencil was then placed on the cloth and covered with charcoal which was rubbed through the perforations. The coloring was done independently.

The paintings of this group exhibit a mixture of Rajput and Mughal styles. The subject matter is Mughal in its recording of themes peculiar to the courts of Akbar and Jahangir, Mughal emperors of India in the sixteenth and seventeenth centuries. But many features demonstrate older Indian traditions including conventions of the Rajput style. These are characterized by the patterned flatness in which figures and settings are treated, the eyes drawn in full view on a face in profile, the attention paid to the minute patterns of textiles and foliage, and the color presented in abstract arrangements.

135

Vishnu

Nepal

Copper, fire-gilt and set with gems

Gift of Frederic B. Pratt

9th century A. D. (?)

H. $9^{11}/_{16}$ in. (24.6 cm)

29.18

The history of Nepali art begins when the gods of India come to Nepal. From the middle of the seventh century, Hinduism as well as Buddhism had set up cult images in this country. The most frequent Hindu type was Vishnu: Vishnu preserves the universe, descending from his transcendental state in order to restore the world when, because of all the evil in it, it is threatened with destruction.

In Nepal, Vishnu is usually accompanied by his consort Laksmi (the Hindu goddess of prosperity) and his carrier, Garuda (the mythical sun-bird represented as part man, part bird). The image in Brooklyn may originally have been part of such a group. The figure was solid-cast in copper, then fire-gilt and encrusted with semi-precious stones of which a few remain. It is archaically conceived with a kind of rigid formalism. The fleshy, short-featured broad face appears as Indian as it is Nepali. A characteristic mannerism of Nepali sculpture is the bulging contour between elbow and wrist. The lotus-discus and club carried in Vishnu's upper arms are his weapons; they are given prominence, by their size, over the cosmic symbols held in his lower hands — the conch in his left and two bosses in the right which replace the traditional lotus.

136

Indra

Nepal
Gilt copper and set with gems
Ella C. Woodward and
Museum Collection Funds

Probably 14th or
15th century A.D.
H. 4¾ in. (12.2 cm)
37.467

Indra, although the Hindu Lord of the Gods, personifies, in Tantric Buddhism, the Buddha of one of the Six Spheres of Existence. He is particularly dear to the myth and art of Nepal. According to Nepali legend, Indra came to earth and stole flowers which his mother in heaven required for a worship. He was caught but, in a shroud of mist, his mother saved him. An image, with hands extended to show that henceforth he will not steal, is set up annually during the Indra festival.

The other type of representation shows him seated, similar to a Bodhisattva figure, in the posture of ease, wearing his broad crown and displaying the horizontal third eye on his forehead. A lotus ascends from Indra's left hand to his shoulder where its open flower carries his weapon, the thunderbolt. Although small in size, this image of Indra is a particularly fine example of metal sculpture.

Masculine Figure

Cambodia

Brown sandstone

Gift of the Rembrandt Club

First Angkor period,

late 9th-12th century A.D.

H. 19½ in. (49.6 cm)

51.237

The Khmers, inhabiting the region of present-day Cambodia, appeared in the third century A.D. as an organized and, more important, as an Indianized people. Sanskrit, Buddhism, and Brahmanism were incorporated into their culture; inspired by the art and ideology of India there was to emerge a new and glorious civilization.

From A.D. 802, when Jayavarman II declared his country's independence of Java and established his capital in the region of Angkor, until the thirteenth century, Cambodian civilization was impressive, with the funerary temple of Angkor Wat (begun early in the twelfth century) standing as the most famed achievement of the Classical period. The sculpture illustrated here, probably a dvarapala or deified guardian, readily attests to the fine craftsmanship of Khmer artists.

Duck-shaped Vessel

China
Cast bronze
Gift of Mr. and
Mrs. Alastair Bradley Martin

Late Chou period,
5th-3rd century B.C.
L. 15 in. (38.1 cm)
H. 11⅛ in. (28.4 cm)
54.145

The manufacture, in China, of bronze vessels fashioned into wine containers and drinking cups began as early as the Shang Dynasty (sixteenth to eleventh century B.C.). They were primarily used as ritual objects and have been preserved in burials. We know, however, from Chinese antiquarians of a much later date that duck vessels were not included among the wine containers listed in ritual texts of the Chou Dynasty (1027-256 B.C.). Since the Brooklyn piece dates from the Late Chou period it seems likely that it served as a domestic or banquet utensil. In a Chinese collector's album of the tenth century is written: "The men of old fashioned these vessels to suggest that wine-drinkers should skim lightly on the surface like ducks and should not become drowned in liquor like a drunkard."

143

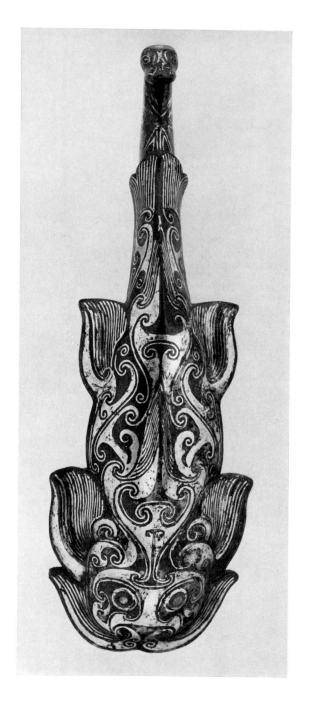

144

Belt Hook

China
Bronze with gold, silver, and
turquoise inlay
Gift of Mr. and
Mrs. Alastair Bradley Martin

Han Dynasty,
about 2nd century B.C.
L. 6⁵/₁₆ in. (17.6 cm)
51.137

During the last centuries of the Chou Dynasty the Chinese came into closer contact with other parts of Asia, and the import of articles and ideas from beyond China's borders increased rapidly.

One article introduced at that time was the belt buckle or clasp. Military techniques imitated from nomads of the steppes seem to have necessitated the adoption of trousers, boots, and belts held together by clasps. This bronze belt hook of the Han Dynasty (206 B.C.-A.D. 220) — in form of a fish terminating in an animal head — is a fine example from a Chinese workshop.

145

Phoenix-headed Ewer

China
Glazed porcelaineous stoneware,
molded and incised design
Frank L. Babbott and
Ella C. Woodward Funds

Probably
10th century A.D.
H. 14⅝ in. (37.2 cm)
54.7

This ewer of high-fired stoneware covered with a transparent glaze may well be a tenth-century (early Sung) or even earlier version of Ch'ing pai — a term for porcelains with pale blue or almost colorless glaze which lies bluest in the hollows or shadows. A ware produced in great quantities in Ch'ing-te-chen (Kiangsi Province) and surrounding areas during Sung and perhaps Yuan times, it is today generally referred to as Ying-ch'ing ware. This piece has come from Indonesia and appears to be an export in its own time, related to the famous phoenix-headed ewer of Chinese white porcelain attributed to the T'ang Dynasty (A.D. 618-906), now in the British Museum. The vessel in Brooklyn may be ascribed to some southern Chinese workshop since ceramic fragments recovered from South China in the 1930's suggest a likely place of origin for the ewer in London.

147

Wine Jar

China
Terracotta-colored clay with
emerald green glaze
Gift of Horace Havemeyer

Liao Dynasty,
A.D. 907-1125
H. 10¾ in. (26.8 cm)
50.162

This ewer is a handsome and representative example of an interesting division of lead-glazed Oriental pottery. Objects of this type have been excavated beyond China's great wall in inner Mongolia and western Manchuria from graves of the Liao Dynasty. They are, therefore, associated with the dynasty that was established by a nomadic group known as the Ch'i-Tan who dominated the lands to the north of China between A.D. 907 and 1125.

The Brooklyn ewer is a wine bottle which derives its shape from leather wine containers mentioned in Chinese literature of the period. It is assumed, however, that such ceramics were simply mortuary representations of the actual objects used in daily life since they are not wine proof: the glaze does not reach the base of the piece, and as the bottom is porous, the bottle could not be put to practical use.

Buddhist Painting

China
Ink and color on silk
Gift of Professor Harold Henderson

Northern Sung Dynasty,
12th century A.D.
51³/₁₆ by 40⅛ in.
(244 by 102 cm)
61.204.30

The extension of Buddhism and its art from India to central Asia or Turkestan began as early as the Indian Kushan period (about A.D. 50-320); but the florescence of Buddhism in China begins in the Six Dynasties period following the invasion of northern China by the To-pa Tartars in A.D. 386. Thereafter, Buddhism influenced the art and religion of China while itself being transformed by Chinese conception.

By the Sung Dynasty, Buddhism had almost entirely lost its vitality in China. Nevertheless, Buddhist sculpture and painting continued to be created. Images of Buddha and his attendants became more personable, no longer remote or inaccessible. In painting and sculpture, figures were conceived with languid, tender gestures, ingratiating smiles, sentimental prettiness, and at the same time greater delicacy of execution. Such superficial refinement can be seen in this painting of the Buddha trinity: swaying grace enhanced by softly flowing garments, elegance of draughtmanship in hair-thin lines combined with the use of gold leaf.

This painting of Buddha attended by two Bodhisattvas is attributed to Chang Ssu Kung, a painter believed to have worked in the Northern Sung period (960-1125). The artist is a rather evasive figure whose name has been preserved only in Japanese records and attached by tradition to a number of Buddhist paintings found mostly in Japanese collections.

150

152

Celadon Bowl

China
Lung Ch'uan Hsien ware
Greyish-white porcelaineous
body with clear celadon glaze
A. Augustus Healy Fund

Sung Dynasty,
A. D. 960-1279
H. 1⅞ in. (4.8 cm)
D. 4¼ in. (10.5 cm)
50.148

Since the seventeenth century celadon, a ware glazed greyish-green with bluish tints, has been generally used to denote that class of Chinese ceramics which had a profound influence on manufacture in other Asian countries. The term, which apparently derives from a costume color in a seventeenth-century French play, can be applied to a variety of greens, running from grey-green and blue-green to a deep sea-green.

This bowl, formerly part of the Imperial Collection in Peking, is an example of fine celadon produced during the Sung Dynasty in Lung Ch'uan Hsien (district), located in the southwestern part of the southern province of Chekiang. It is characterized, along with other more typical, heavier Lung Ch'uan celadons, by a greyish-white porcelaineous body, burnt red where unprotected by the glaze. The glaze is of a bubbly consistency, causing a softness of texture and greater refraction of light than is found in many other types of glazes.

Oviform Jar

China
Porcelain with blue underglaze painting
Gift of the executors of the estate
of Augustus S. Hutchins

Yuan Dynasty,
14th century A.D.
H. 11^{13}/$_{16}$ in. (30 cm)
52.87.1

So called "Chinese blue and white" is simply porcelain with cobalt blue decoration under a transparent glaze. The Chinese were not the first to use this method as technically similar ceramics have been found in the Near East, dating from the ninth century. The introduction of this technique in China seems to stem from the period of Mongol domination during the Yuan Dynasty (A.D. 1279-1368) when heavy trading existed between eastern and western Asia.

The history of Chinese "blue and white," perhaps the most widespread and popular of all forms of ceramic decoration, is inseparably linked with Chinese porcelain of the Ming period. "Blue and white" Yuan Dynasty porcelain of the fourteenth century is characterized by an imperfect blackish blue color, and its design and drawing are akin to painting of the Sung and Yuan periods. Two jars with decoration similar to this one are known, one in Tokyo and one in Istanbul. Probably made at Ching-te-chen kilns at the end of the Yuan period, this "kuan" is certainly the finest example of its type known.

154

155

Plate

China
Porcelain, blue underglaze painting
Samuel P. Avery Fund

Ming Dynasty,
about A. D. 1400-1430
D. 15¾ in. (40 cm)
51.85

This blue and white plate is decorated with tree peonies, symbolic of spring. Lotus-flower scrolls representing summer fruits and flowers of the season encircle the central motif. Only blue and whites made for the Chinese Imperial Palace in the early years of the Ming Dynasty (1368-1644) demonstrate such technical perfection as evident in this plate.

It has a particular characteristic which identifies it with early fifteenth-century blue and whites: the cobalt blue, heaped on under the glaze, varies in density over the surface, causing it to turn black.

158

Orchid, Bamboo, and Thorn

by Hsüeh Ch'uang
China
Ink on paper
A. Augustus Healy and
M. T. Cockroft Funds and
Anonymous Donor

Yuan Dynasty,
A.D. 1279-1368
15¾ by 25³/₁₆ in.
(40 by 64 cm)
52.50

A seven-character inscription on the painting tells that "Hsüeh Ch'uang made (painted) a gentle breeze turn the orchids (or Hsüeh Ch'uang made orchids turning in sunlit breeze)."

The symbolism of orchid painting seemed to have played a very important role in the culture of Yuan Dynasty China which had been conquered by the Mongols. The orchid signified a strong sense of loyalty in spite of adversity, and it was identified with the princely man, a noble-minded literatus, as bamboo was a symbol of the perfect gentleman. Among the literati who retired from government service after the fall of the Sung Dynasty, rather than serving their Mongol conquerors, the orchid symbolized attachment to Sung and rejection of Yuan rule. Its combination with the thorn might have referred to the troubles and adversities it encountered. But the orchid had become such a popular subject in the Yuan Dynasty that it appealed to large numbers of artists, Sung loyalists or not.

The artist Hsüeh Ch'uang (Snowy Window) was connected with two Ch'an temples in Suchou, Chekiang Province. His fame as an orchid painter grew steadily; yet soon after his death, he seemed to have been entirely forgotten in China. Instead, his paintings were well received in Japan, and his influence more strongly felt there, undoubtedly because Japanese Zen priests arranged for his paintings to be imported from China.

159

Landscape Scroll

by Ch'ien Ku (1508-1572)
China
Ink and color on paper
A. Augustus Healy, Polhemus, and
Museum Collection Funds

Ming Dynasty,
dated A. D. 1556
H. 10⅞ in. (27.7 cm)
L. of total scroll 50¾ in.
(129 cm)
55.97

This scroll shows a scholar approaching the Ping Po Pavilion where another scholar and servant await. It begins with three large characters written in ink on blue paper by the painter, poet and calligrapher, Wang Ku-Hsiang (1501-1568). A fourteen-character inscription completes the painting: "In the lengthening days of the Ping Ch'en year of the era of Chia Ching (A. D. 1556), Ch'ien Ku painted the Ping Po Pavilion picture." The painting is followed by seven poems — all by men believed to be contemporary with the artist who was a pupil of the famous Ming Dynasty painter Wen Cheng-Ming.

The precise significance of the theme of this painting is not known. It may refer to a certain Hsu-Ch'ien of the Yuan Dynasty, a distinguished non-conformist of his time, for whom the Ping Po Pavilion was apparently a place of seclusion. Possibly because of political problems in the sixteenth century, Hsu's earlier non-conformity was a source of inspiration for Ch'ien Ku and the poets whose poems were included in the scroll.

Ewer

Korea
Glazed stoneware
Gift of Mrs. Darwin R. James III

Koryu Dynasty,
A.D. 918-1392
H. 7 in. (17.6 cm)
56.138.1

The bulk of the ceramic production during the Korean Koryu Dynasty is celadon ware. It combines an earlier ash-glaze tradition with new pottery techniques which may have come from China in the tenth century; but the height of greatest activity and technical perfection was reached two hundred years later.

This ewer, perhaps a stubby version of a wine pot, is covered with an incised pattern of lotus leaves. Another design, the edges of which have been heightened with dots of white slip, fills the center of the lotus leaves. The handle is decorated by incising as well as by dotting with slip and appliqué to suggest bent and tied bamboo. The entire pot is covered with a celadon glaze fired to a blue-green. The piece has been tentatively ascribed to the Yuch'on-in kilns in the P'uan district on the southwest coast of Korea, as its decoration is similar to documented fragments discovered at the site in 1929.

162

163

Painting of a Local Korean God

by Kim Myong-Kuk (Yun Tam)
Korea
Ink on paper
Gift of Mrs. Robert van Roejen

Li Dynasty,
A.D. 1623-1649
20½ by 10½ in.
(52 by 27 cm)
59.26

In Korea, as in China and Japan, the art of painting was practiced in two different circles: one was made up of the professional artists who were members of the Government Office of Arts, the other included amateurs or scholars, men of letters or politicians who took up painting as an avocation and as a means of displaying their talents.

Kim Myong-Kuk served as a member of the Government Office of Arts and was a teacher there. Eventually, however, he became an independent painter and is now known particularly for his figurative compositions. As a member of diplomatic missions, Kim Myong-Kuk frequently visited Japan whose art exerted a strong influence on his work. This painting of a local Korean god of fortune, Po Dai, is done with rapid but elegant brushstrokes and reflects the artist's ability to depict his subjects with the utmost economy of line. It is signed "The Ancient Drunkard" above the artist's seal.

164

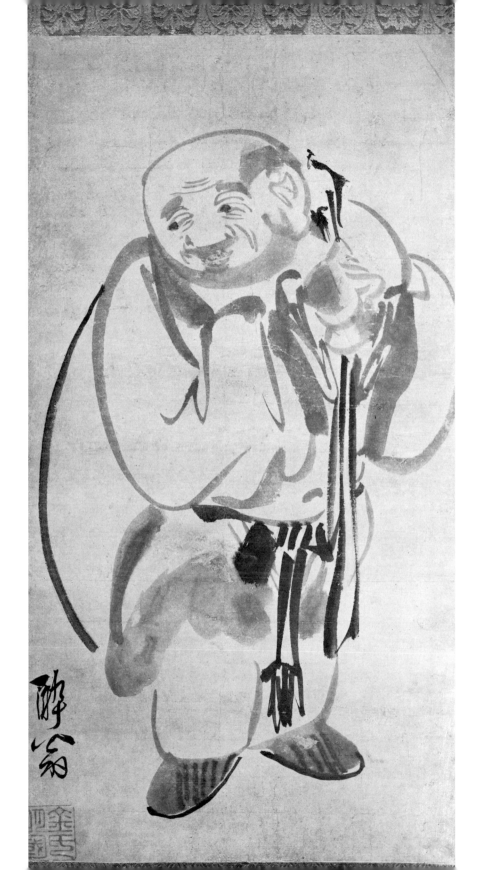

Bodhisattva

Japan
Wood
Frank L. Babbott Fund

Jogan period,
probably second half
of the 9th century A.D.
H. $15^9/_{16}$ in. (39.5 cm)
56.153

Buddhism was introduced into Japan from Korea in the sixth century A.D. Its ultimate victory over Shintoism was of extreme cultural importance, making the church a major patron of the arts for centuries.

By the ninth century, Japanese Buddhist sculpture, which hitherto had been fashioned in many media, was now made, as a rule, of wood; usually the whole piece was carved out of a single block. Although much of the surface is covered with darkened laquer, this figure appears to be carved from Japanese cypress. It demonstrates most of the special traits of the ninth-century style: solemn expression, fat cheeks, contour lines indicating a muscular division of chest and abdomen, many sharply cut parallel lines of carefully patterned drapery, as well as the characteristic massiveness and heavy sensuousness of Indian art.

Since part of the left hand is missing, definite iconographic identification is not possible. It seems likely, however, that the figure represents a Sho Kwannon, a deity of Indian Brahmin origin, who had been assimilated into Buddhism and treated as a Bosatsu (Bodhisattva).

166

火

Drawing of Kayosei

Japan
Ink on paper
Frank L. Babbott, Carll H. De Silver, and
Caroline A. L. Pratt Funds

Heian period, 11th or
early 12th century A.D.
21½ by 11¼ in.
(54.5 by 28.5 cm)
59.177

Iconographic drawings, first imported from China, furnished detailed models for wood and metal sculpture of Buddhist icons. In Japan, under the doctrinal influence of the Shingon and Tendai sects, such drawings and sculpture underwent radical developments, and many complicated types were added, especially during the late Heian period. Original iconographic drawings of that time are exceedingly rare; they are, however, represented by a characteristic example here, which shows the strong, iron-wire line and linear rhythm so typical of this period.

The subject represents Kayosei, one of the seven constellations which include sun, moon, and five stars of which Kayosei is one. The source text for these deities, which — although Buddhist — are rooted in the astrological magico-religion of the Chinese Han Dynasty, is the Sutra (Book) of the Constellations. The latter explains that the seven constellations shine among the Gods of Heaven but below change into human forms. They each appear in the ascendance for a day, making a complete sequence in seven days. The day during which Kayosei is ascendant, is an auspicious time to punish criminals, catch thieves, perform frauds and deceits, buy gold, sheep and cattle, move armed troops, and acquire military weapons. And if one acts to suppress robbers, "one will unfailingly triumph against them."

Taizokai Mandara (Womb-world)

Japan
Painting in colors and gold on silk
Museum Collection Fund

Kamakura period,
13th century A. D.
$89^7/_{16}$ by $56^5/_{16}$ in.
(228 by 143 cm)
21.240.2

Pictures of Buddhist deities arranged in geometric patterns are typical of esoteric Buddhism whose teaching could be explained more easily in pictures than in words. They are the principal objects displayed in the temples of the Shingon, or "True Word," sect of Buddhism, introduced into Japan from China by Kukai (774-835). Shingon distinguished revealed doctrines, taught by the historic Buddha, from those secret doctrines of the "Great Illuminator," the Buddha Dainichi.

Shingon also juxtaposed a spiritual or eternal world to a material world. Double mandara paintings of the forces of the eternal world and of the material, or womb, world (Taizokai) were created to express this concept. The Taizokai mandara shown here represents the realm of forms and its dynamic activity, while its companion, also in the Museum's collection, represents the static realm of ideas. In the

170

center is Dainichi seated on a lotus pedestal within a circle. From this circle emanate eight lotus petals divided by thunder bolts, and each petal contains one of the four Dhyani Buddhas or his Bodhisattva. Above them is a triangle topped by leaf-shaped devices each containing a swastika, symbolizing matter. Three rows of Buddhist divinities and an outer row of smaller figures, all arranged in hieratic fashion, are emanations of Dainichi.

173

Fragment from the Kitano Honji Engi

Japan   14th century A.D.
Ink on paper   11 by 18¹³/₁₆ in.
Frank L. Babbott Fund   (28 by 47.8 cm)
                                           57.171

Narrative scroll painting is a distinct and peculiar art form in Japan.
The technique of implementing the understanding of a story with
painting originated on the mainland, but developed more fully in
Japan. Although the earliest Japanese examples date from the eighth
century, an outburst of narrative painting begins in the twelfth century and continues into later times.

This fragment was part of a scroll containing the tales of the founding of the Kitano temple. The building was dedicated to Sugawara-
no-Michizane (A.D. 845-903) who was a famous patriot in Japanese
history serving as a high government official until forced into exile
by the political machinations of the Fujiwara family. After his death
the charges were repudiated, and his reputation was restored. According to legend, however, the spirit of Michizane remained irate and
caused catastrophies to plague the court at Kyoto. In 947, a shrine
was established in the hope of appeasing his spirit, but apparently
this was without success since one night, when a palace was being
constructed at Kyoto, the ghost of Michizane created mysterious
wormholes in the timbers for the building. The Brooklyn fragment
depicts the discovery of the imperfect timbers the following morning
and the effect of this discovery on the carpenters and courtiers.

174

175

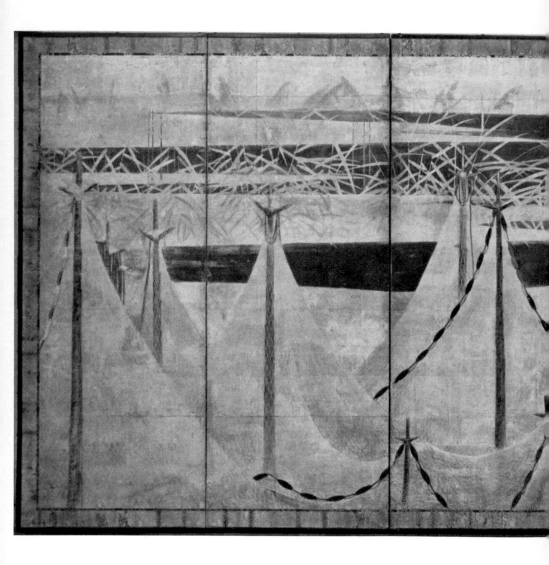

176

177

Drying Fish Nets

One of a pair of screens
by Kaiho Yusho (1533-1615)
Japan
Color on paper, pasted over with gold foil
Carll H. De Silver and
Ella C. Woodward Funds

Momoyama period,
A. D. 1568-1615
65¾ by 111¹/₁₆ in.
(167 by 282.2 cm)
59.7.1,2

Large screens, decorated with calligraphy, landscapes, and many other subjects derived from nature, illustrate two basic types of Japanese painting: the calligraphic black-ink style derived from China and introduced with Zen Buddhism in the thirteenth century, and the colorful, sensuous, national style called Yamato-e (literally "Japanese painting") which became assimilated at an early date so that its source in seventh-century China was virtually forgotten. Yamato-e blossomed during the Momoyama period and continued well into the Edo period (1616-1868) when Japan's best artists were called upon to decorate and brighten the vast interior spaces of many stone castles in which painted screens either served as walls or were folded and portable. A new painting style developed to meet the special demand of the setting; the use of gold leaf as background was particularly popular since it reflected light handsomely and imparted splendor and magnificence to the gloomy interiors.

Kaiho Yusho painted screens both in rich colors suited to castle apartments, and in quieter ink tones more generally favored for the decoration of temple rooms. The subject matter, drying fish nets, is clearly indicated as is the theme of the Four Seasons depicted by changes in the nets and grasses. Two other pairs of screens with the same subject and attributed to Kaiho Yusho are preserved in Japanese collections.

179

Screen

Japan
Colors and ink on paper with
gold embossing
Gift of Frederic B. Pratt

Edo period,
17th century A.D.
39⅜ by 107⅞ in.
(100 by 269 cm)
39.87

During the late sixteenth and early seventeenth centuries, genre painting, usually mounted on screens, became increasingly popular due to the social disorders of the late Muromachi period when the rise of the commercial and industrial class created an urban civilization. From this time on, bustling city life became an independent theme for secular painters, or machieshi, who specialized in screens decorated with genre scenes. In response to public taste, interest shifted from general views to detailed renderings of figurative subjects, mainly of beautiful women. Courtesans and dancing girls, or yuna (women of easy virtue who worked in the hot baths), played a leading part in compositions, evidence of the free, even licentious, manners of a period which gave rise to pleasure haunts and gay quarters in the cities.

The Museum's screen shows a lively group of bath women being taken on a gay trip into the country. They wear the kosode, a gaudy short-sleeved kimono with a thin belt. The unknown artist who produced this screen was a keen-eyed observer who gave each figure a characteristic physiognomy, pose, and manner which evoke the whole tenor of their lives.

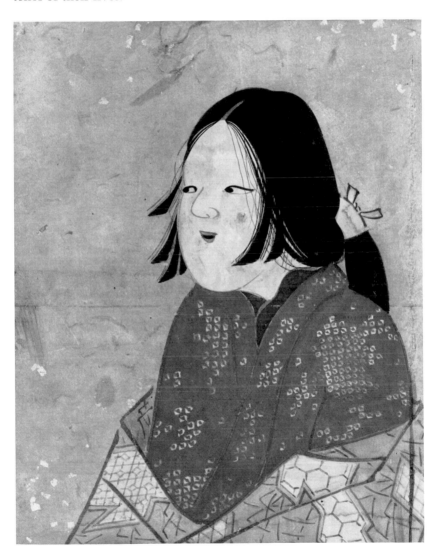

Landscape Scroll

Section of a six-fold screen
by Ike-no Taiga (1723-1776)
Japan
Ink on paper
Gift of Mr. and Mrs. Carl Selden

Middle Edo period
70 by 20½ in.
(200 by 52 cm)
64.6

Ike-no Taiga, a poet and student of Zen Buddhist doctrine, was the first great painter of the Japanese Nanga school, a term used to designate the work of non-professional artists who were primarily literary men. Originally derived from a literary movement of poet-painters in China during the Yuan Dynasty (1279-1368) the individualistic Nanga artists, rejecting academic conventions, sought to project their feelings and personal moods.

This landscape, painted in the calligraphic black-ink style derived from China, possibly represents a view of a place in Japan. It was originally part of a folding screen the panels of which have now been separated. A second section of the screen can be seen in the scroll of calligraphy in the following illustration. The landscape shows the style of Taiga's mature works with its nervous, bold outline and masses of light, feathery brushstrokes creating a stippling effect.

Scroll of Calligraphy

Section of a six-fold screen
by Ike-no Taiga (1723-1776)
Japan
Ink on paper
Gift of Samuel Hammer

Middle Edo period
52½ by 20⅜ in.
(133.2 by 51.8 cm)
64.157

In the Far East, calligraphy ranked above the painter's art. A piece of calligraphy is made up of a number of characters or words, each of which is composed of a number of strokes. Each brushstroke has a role to play in the total harmony. It must be in its proper place and sequence, must be excellent in itself, and cannot be corrected after it is made. Moreover, the division of space and the over-all composition are, as in painting, of major importance.

Since many Chinese characters or their constituents were originally pictographs, it was easy for Chinese script to become a popular art form. Calligraphy was equally important in Japan after the introduction of Chinese script in A.D. 552. By that time, however, it had already undergone various changes. Its early archaic form, found on bones and shells, was used for divination purposes by ancient diviners. By the end of the sixth century a standard style had developed as well as cursive variations, including a running script and "grass" writing.

In both countries, great masters distinguished themselves in the arts of painting as well as of calligraphy; the latter was generally considered essential to the training of a scholar. Purportedly, Ike-no Taiga already excelled in calligraphy at the age of seven and was famed in his maturity for his bold style. The scroll illustrated here reads:

> The shadow of the stone   The sound of the spring
> The red pavilion   Encompasses the jade lute.

188

189

Landscape

One of a pair of small screens
by Maruyama Okyo (1733-1798)
Japan
Ink, color, and gold on paper
Gift of Dr. and
Mrs. Frank L. Babbott, Jr.

Middle Edo period
21⅝ by 69⅞ in.
(54.8 by 177.5 cm)
54.102.8,9

In the eighteenth century, new trends emerged in Japanese painting; particularly notable was the realistic movement of the Maruyama Shijo school of which Maruyama Okyo was the first exponent. Inspired by actual scenes in Japan, particularly the countryside around Kyoto, he conveyed the real forms of objects by means of precise and subtle drawing and nuances of ink and colors while at the same time maintaining the open, unlimited space peculiar to Far Eastern painting.

These screens, used for the annual Japanese doll festival, represent the changing seasons, from the white spring blossoms of the cherry trees in the right of one screen (not illustrated), through the winter whiteness capping Mt. Fuji in the left of the other.

Noh Robe

Japan
Painted silk with orange lining
Gift from the Hammer Foundation

Edo period
late 17th to early
18th century
L. 62 in. (157.5 cm)
53.181

The Noh drama is the classical drama of the aristocracy (as contrasted with the popular form known as Kabuki). It developed out of
the music and dances of religious ceremonies or scenes from ancient
folk tales, and it deals with the world of gods and heroes. The action
is highly stylized and resembles, in its use of chorus and masks,
ancient Greek drama.

One of its distinguishing features are the costumes the gorgeous-
ness of which contrasts sharply with the severely controlled course of
action, the subtle text, and the restrained movement. These costumes
reached a high artistic level during the Momoyama (1573-1615) and
Edo (1615-1868) periods. Richly decorated, they were enhanced by
the idealized, almost expressionless, masks worn by the actors. Some
costumes were designed and executed by important artists although,
with few exceptions, the attributions to individual artists are based
on uncertain traditions. The design on this robe, a painting of pine,
bamboo and prunus, is ascribed to the famous painter Ogata Korin
(1658-1716). The motif, referred to as "the three friends," was
favored both in China and Japan, signifying strength, resiliency or
pliancy, and courage.

192

Primitive Art
and
New World Cultures

Ceremonial Pipe

Tennessee or Georgia, Temple Mound I   A.D. 700-1000
Sandstone   H. 4¾ in. (12.2 cm)
Henry L. Batterman and   37.2802
Frank S. Benson Funds

Popular concepts of Indian art in terms of arrowheads and bead-work do scant justice to the succession of high cultures that once existed in various parts of North America. The Temple Mound period saw the rise of important centers in the Mississippi Valley. Large courts and pyramid-based temples show the same relationship with contemporary civilizations of Mexico as the burial offerings of fine pottery, engraved shell, copperwork, and small stone sculpture.

This crouching figure with its sensitively modeled face formed the bowl of a ceremonial pipe. Its size and weight emphasize the fact that tobacco smoking, which originated here, had a ritual significance among the Indians that was lost when the rest of the world adopted it.

The pipe has a long and distinguished history. Though no record remains of its discovery, it has been known for more than a century and a half. Among its earlier owners was the great naturalist Alexander von Humboldt. He published a drawing of it in 1814 in the two-volume work that acquainted Europe with the cultural achievements of ancient America.

196

197

Mask

Kuskokwin region, Alaska, Eskimo
Painted wood

Late 19th century
H. 15¾ in. (40 cm)
44.34.7

Survival in the Arctic does not preclude the leisure that art requires, but rather enforces it at certain times, creating a special need. With the materials available, the Eskimo fashions everyday articles and dramatic ceremonial equipment often with exceptionally fine craftsmanship. The masks made for religious and secular occasions are often striking but fragile because they were not intended to be used a second time.

Masks for the hunting festivals held at various times of the year represented the spirits of the animals in an imaginative combination of symbolic and realistic forms. The mask pictured here is a type worn at ceremonies related to the hunting of the Valley Ptarmigan in the spring. The design incorporates easily recognizable parts of the bird. Its head is set on the forehead of the symbolic face, claws extend from either side of the mouth, the tail hangs from the chin, and feathers encircle the head. The wooden parts are painted white, black, and reddish brown.

198

Thunderbird Mask

Vancouver Island, British Columbia,
Kwakiutl
Painted wood
Museum Expedition

Late 19th century
H. 22 in. (56.6 cm)
08.479

Along the Northwest Coast, natural wealth supported a rich, stratified society. A class of professional artists created household objects of great elegance and filled the requirements of an elaborate ceremonial life. Their products, ranging from great totem poles to delicate carvings in ivory, antler, and argillite, conform to a homogeneous and sophisticated style based on formalized representations of ancestral totemic animal spirits.

Masks, as important in the rituals of Northwest Coast tribes as among the Eskimo and many other American peoples, took especially spectacular forms. The Kwakiutl excelled in devising masks that had movable parts and hinged sections. During the winter months, masks like this came to life at firelight ceremonials and displayed their magic. The great somber head of the Thunderbird, or eagle, swings open dramatically to reveal other mythological figures vividly painted in red, black, white, and blue. The dominant figure of Sisiutl, the double-headed serpent, stretches nearly sixteen feet wide.

202

Robe

Plains Indians (probably Shoshone)
Painted elk skin
Dick S. Ramsay Fund

Late 19th century
72 in. square (182 cm)
64.13

Men of the Plains Indian tribes decorated their buffalo, elk, and deer hide robes with realistically painted narrative scenes. This lively composition is thought to be the work of Washakie, an especially talented Shoshone whose robes are now in several other collections.

The central portion of the robe illustrates the Sun Dance, the most conspicuous religious festival of the Plains Indians. At this time, the tepees are arranged in a large circle, and the tribe, which has been scattered in small bands for the winter months, finally unites for the celebration. For those who have pledged to hold the ceremony, there is the burden of fasting as well as the sacred pole dance, which often involves self-torture. The surrounding designs of the robe show a buffalo hunt and its results: mounted warriors pursuing the huge animals with bows and arrows and several buffalo carcasses being dressed.

By the late nineteenth century, trade pigments had largely replaced the colors formerly derived from native plants and minerals. They were applied with an instrument made of porous bone.

Kachina Doll and Mask

New Mexico, Zuñi
Cotton fabric, fiber, wool, and feathers;
painted wood and leather
Museum Expedition

Late 19th century
H. doll 20⅞ in. (53 cm)
H. mask 9⅝ in. (25 cm)
03.130, 04.196

Pueblo tribes of the American Southwest try to maintain and express the traditional values of their people through the drama and color of the Kachina cult. Outstanding masks and dolls of the Zuñi were at their best at the turn of the century, when the Museum's collection was formed.

206

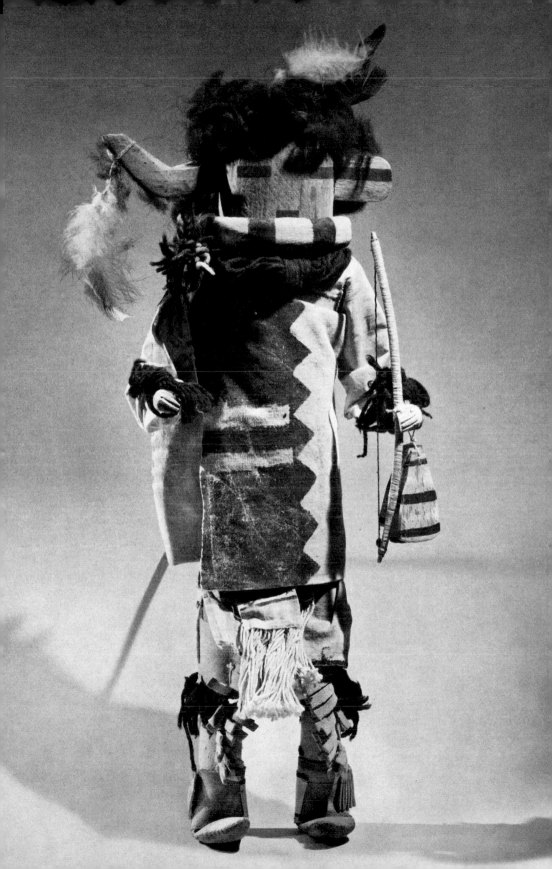

Zuñi "masked gods" and other supernaturals traditionally live and dance at the bottom of a sacred lake, but like to come back to Zuñi and dance in ceremonial reenactments of their glorious feats. The priests, who make and don the masks and costumes of the deities, are thought to assume the spirit of the god along with his appearance. If the gods are pleased with every detail of the ritual they will grant the people their blessings and provide rain. Kachina dolls, given to the children during the ceremonies, familiarize them with the appearance and identity of each of the gods.

The doll and mask pictured here represent Sayatasha, the Rain Priest of the north, a member of the Council of Gods. Sayatasha is distinguished by a blue horn extending from the side of his head.

Mask

Central Mexico, Teotihuacan
Dark green stone
A. Augustus Healy Fund

A. D. 200-600
H. 5¼ in. (13.5 cm)
50.150

Teotihuacan, the ancient metropolis about an hour's drive north of Mexico City, is famous for the majesty of its ordered pyramids and the still lively colors of its frescoed rooms. During the centuries of its ascendancy it was the largest city of Mesoamerica, and its influence was felt throughout Mexico and even in the great Maya centers farther south.

More than any other art form, the stone masks of Classic Teotihuacan style express the grandeur of the civilization that produced them. Sensitively modeled but impersonal, they seem to look out of the past with an empty gaze that is more solemn than their original aspect, when the inlaid eyes and teeth were in place.

The masks were not intended to be worn; they lack the necessary openings in the eyes, and some are far too large and heavy. Nevertheless, the perforations, usually in the temples and jaw as well as in the earlobes for ornaments, show that they were meant to be attached to something — perhaps to cult figures or to the dead for burial.

210

The Goddess Chicomecoatl

Mexico, Aztec
Volcanic stone
A. Augustus Healy Fund

15th century A.D.
H. 15 in. (38 cm)
51.109

The forthright, realistic quality of Aztec sculpture seems to reflect the driving force that carried the lowly Aztec tribe to a position of dominance over most of Mexico in only a hundred years. As their power grew, they incorporated the gods and goddesses of conquered peoples into a complex and ever-expanding pantheon. These deities, transformed into full Aztec style, were represented in the temples and altars of provincial centers as well as the capital city.

Chicomecoatl, an Aztec goddess of maize or corn, probably descended from the fertility goddesses of the first people who cultivated the all-important crop in the Valley of Mexico. She was considered a sister of Tlaloc, the rain god, whose antecedents were different but equally ancient. She is shown in this well-known relief with her special attributes, the two maize ears in her headdress and the serpent staff. The latter refers to her calendar name, Seven Serpent, which also had the meaning of maize.

212

Lienzo of Ihuitlán

Oaxaca, Mexico, Mixtec
Painted cotton cloth
Carll H. De Silver Fund

A. D. 1500-1550
H. 95½ in. (243 cm)
W. 60 in. (152 cm)
42.160

Only in Middle America did the peoples of the New World develop writing of any kind. When the Spaniards reached Mexico, a semi-ideographic system was in use for keeping historical, religious, commercial, and government records; a map of the country was among Montezuma's gifts to Cortez.

Painted within 30 years or so after the Conquest, the Lienzo of Ihuitlán is a map-like genealogical record of the interrelated families that ruled all southern Puebla and northern Oaxaca. Its outstanding documentary value, rarity, and fine draughtsmanship make it the most important of the Museum's five Mexican pictorial manuscripts.

214

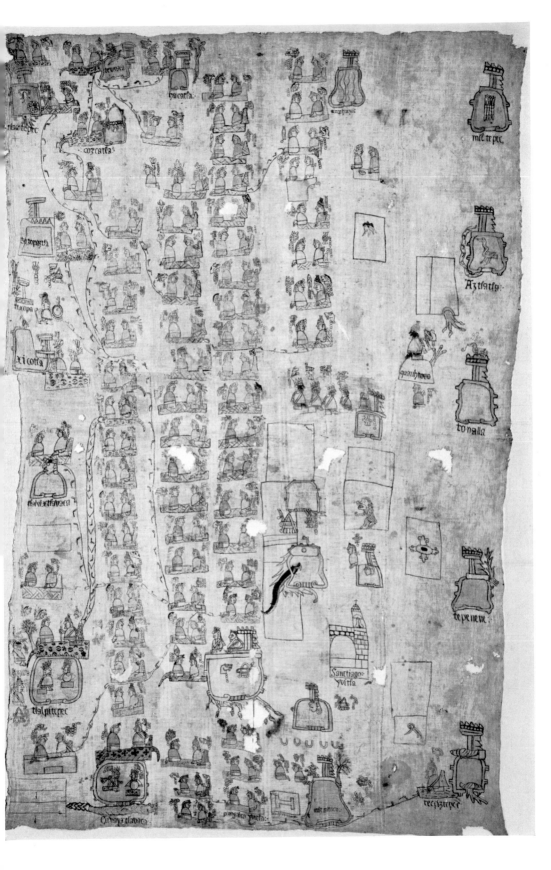

The Lienzo, made up of nine individually woven strips of cotton, has black lettering and outlines with washes of pale red, yellow, and greenish blue. It shows the husband and wife of each generation seated on a mat or jaguar skin, ancient signs of rank, with a name symbol painted beside each figure. There are 170, arranged in columns according to dynasties and connected by rows of footprints to indicate how certain rulers were descended from those of other towns. Twenty-one place names are marked in Spanish script, but the only other European element in the painting is the church of Santiago Ihuitlán, shown at lower right below its Mixtec place-glyph.

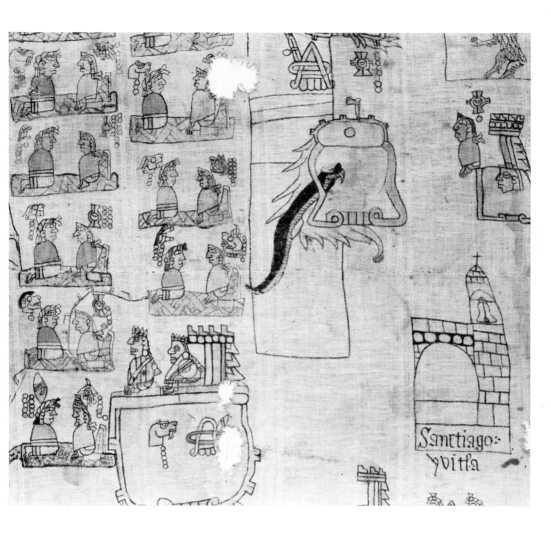

Santiago: yvitla

217

Quetzalcoatl

San Vicente Tancuayalab, eastern
Mexico, Huastec
Limestone
Henry L. Batterman and
Frank S. Benson Funds

A. D. 900-1250
H. 62¼ in. (158 cm)
37.2897

The Huasteca was settled by people of Maya speech, but it was so
long cut off from the central Maya area that by Postclassic times
their artistic tradition retained little trace of its origin. This life-size
figure discovered in the 1840's has become world famous as a classic
statement of the late Huastec style. The precise solidity of the form
is relieved by cut-out areas and delicate facial modeling, lightened by
the tracery of incised surface pattern.

Semicircular headdresses appear on many Huastec figures, but the
added conical elements identify the representation as Quetzalcoatl,
the "Feathered Serpent." The beneficent creator god, long revered

218

in many parts of Mesoamerica, had merged with the identity of the Toltec culture hero and taken on a complexity of forms and associations. Quetzalcoatl was identified with the planet Venus in its dual aspect as morning and evening star. The skeleton bound to the back of the figure may symbolize the passage of Venus through the world of the dead during the period when it is gone from the sky. Incised serpent heads and ears of maize refer to Quetzalcoatl's role as the founder of agriculture.

Tripod Vase

Petén, Guatemala, Maya
Pottery
Dick S. Ramsay Fund

A.D. 400-600
H. 8⅜ in. (21.5 cm)
65.155

The Maya are one of the enduring mysteries of ancient America. No one understands why native culture reached its peak in the flat, seemingly endless jungle that centers in northern Guatemala, or why it receded leaving only a thinly scattered population of the same stock that had brought civilization to so unlikely a region. The history recorded in Maya hieroglyphic writing still awaits decipherment, but in most texts the dates, calculations, and astronomical information can be read, and in some the names of persons, places, and certain kinds of events.

The inscription that appears here, though unreadable and perhaps only decorative, is composed of familiar glyphic elements which are datable stylistically around the sixth century. On the back of the vase there is another cartouche of four glyphs, two of them identical, and on one side appears a larger, single glyph.

Cylindrical tripod bowls are characteristic of Teotihuacan, and their appearance in the Maya area marks the period of strong influence from the Valley of Mexico. This unusually large tripod is nevertheless typical of early Maya ware. A glossy slip of variegated black and orange-brown covers the reddish clay except on the rounded bottom and hollow, cut-out feet. The glyphs were incised through the slip before polishing and firing.

222

223

Carved Pendant

Chiapas, Mexico, Maya
Jade
Frank L. Babbott Fund

Mid-8th century A.D.
H. 3⅜ in. (8.5 cm)
36.268

At the time of the Conquest, Spanish eagerness for gold appeared eccentric to native peoples accustomed for over 2,000 years to value jade above all other materials. The difference in values led to an unexpectedly fair exchange at least once. The party exploring the Gulf Coast in 1518 bartered briskly for three days trading glass beads, especially the green ones, for the Indians' polished axe heads, which shone like gold. But, as Bernal Diaz noted wryly, *"las hachas eran de cobre puro, y las cuentas un poco de nada"* ("the axes were pure copper and the beads, a little bit of nothing utterly worthless").

Maya jadeworkers left evidence of the great value placed on jade in earlier times. Their ornaments often have uneven shapes that resulted not from any lack of technical mastery but from reluctance to remove any more of the precious material than necessary or sacrifice excellence of color for symmetry.

Traditional among the Maya were jade pendants carved with a face that has large ear ornaments and an elaborate symbolic headdress. They reflect changing modes and techniques through the centuries. Ours, from the Ornate Phase of the Late Classic period, belongs to a small group distinguished by headdresses that symbolize the maize plant.

225

Dancing Figures

Las Mercedes, Costa Rica
Grey volcanic stone
Alfred W. Jenkins Fund

13th-16th century A.D.
H. of stela 22 in. (56 cm)
H. of figures 10¼ in. (26 cm)
34.5094

Costa Rica and Panama together are smaller than New York State, yet the distinctive polychrome ceramics, stone sculpture, jade, and goldwork found in such abundance there are admired in museums and private collections all over the world. Such evidence of prosperity hints at the extent of maritime trade that must have passed along this narrow link between the continents in ancient times, adding to its natural wealth, which included the prized purple dye (like Tyrian purple) extracted from sea snails. While it also profited by new ideas from the great centers far to the north and south, lower Central America remained politically and artistically independent.

Interest in Costa Rican archaeology was aroused in the late nineteenth century by the collection of Minor C. Keith made when he was building the country's first railroad across the Atlantic lowlands. A site on his hacienda, Las Mercedes, yielded many of the finest sculptures. The nearly 4,000 pieces now in Brooklyn provide a unique opportunity to study the rich ancient culture of this country.

Paired Crocodile Gods

Parita, Panama
Cast gold with inlaid resin and shell
Alfred W. Jenkins Fund

A.D. 700-1500
H. 4⅛ in. (10.5 cm)
64.33.1

There is no evidence of metalworking in Mexico or Guatemala before the tenth century, long after goldworking in particular had reached a high level of craftsmanship in Central and South America. Though generally used alone, gold was occasionally combined with other materials, as in this pendant designed for inlays in both the club-heads and the waists of the figures. The tusk-shaped bodies of copal resin, although ancient, are not the original inserts, which may have been of the same material or of whale-tooth ivory, bone, or serpentine. The shell club-heads are recent replacements.

The casting was done by the lost-wax process customarily employed by Panamanian goldworkers. Of particular interest is the way each figure was cast separately with its own pair of suspension loops. They are joined by an elaborate set of rods and hooks which were provided for in the original wax models and cast as part of the figures. This unusual construction may have been employed to allow the figures to be separated for use as individual pendants. Another possibility is that the artist wished to overcome the difficulties presented in casting such an intricate shape in one operation where the risk of spoiling both figures was greater.

Burial Urn

Marajo Island, Brazil
Pottery
Museum Expedition

A.D. 1000-1200
H. 41¾ in. (106 cm)
33.675

A vast river network unites all of northeastern South America from the Andes to the Atlantic coast, making communication and travel relatively easy. Conditions of life in the Equatorial forest, however, worked against cultural advancement, and settlers with a more complex social system could not maintain it for many generations. One such group, from the upper reaches of the Amazon, established colonies about the year 1000 on the Island of Marajo, in the river delta. Mounds that still rise well above the level of annual flooding mark their dwelling and burial sites. Handsome ceramics, ranging from miniature vessels to great burial urns, trace the gradual decline of Marajo society until its eventual replacement by simpler cultures.

The Marajoara style is noted for complex surface patterns achieved by polychrome painting or by an unusual method of incising and carving to produce a shallow two-plane relief. It was sometimes enhanced by layers of colored slip or a fill of contrasting pigment to create a kind of champlevé. Modeling, employed sparingly, completes the effect of richness. The particularly large painted urn shown here in profile has two effigy faces and two modeled figures as handles. Its size proves the potter's skill and also the strengthening effect of the unusual tempering material customarily added to the clay, a tree bark containing silica.

Flask with Relief Figures

Middle Cauca Valley, Colombia,
Quimbaya
Cast gold-copper alloy, tumbaga
Alfred W. Jenkins Fund

A.D. 500-1000
H. 8 in. (20.3 cm)
35.507

The word "Eldorado," accepted by Webster as "any place or realm of fabulous richness," comes from a widely spread legend that originated in Colombia. Archaeological finds amply confirm Colombia's ancient wealth in gold. They also suggest that goldworking in the Americas may have begun there, and that the technique of lost-wax casting did undoubtedly originate in this region. Certainly the Quimbaya goldsmiths carried the technique to its height: they were the only craftsmen to attempt the casting of entire vessels.

Of the 20 or so known, nearly all are shapely, narrow-necked flasks or human effigies. This sumptuous vessel combines the two modes, with male and female figures in low relief. Its sweeping rhythmic forms are interrupted only at the base of the neck, thinned to accommodate a heavy suspension cord or a multiple-strand necklace. Several of the figural vessels show flasks worn as pendants or held in hands.

Usually the hands were cast separately. During the casting of the vase, core supports were set in the wrist openings to hold the core in place within the outer mold, after the wax had been melted out and before the gold was poured in to replace it. Four other core-support openings in the base and upper lobes were plugged with gold disks.

233

234

Mask

Chinca, northern Ecuador, Bahia   500 B. C. - A. D. 500
Pottery   H. 5⅜ in. (13.7 cm)
Charles Stewart Smith Memorial Fund   35.1860

Coastal Ecuador has long been noted for the variety and beauty of the pottery found there, especially the countless modeled and mold-made figurines. Recent archaeological studies in the south have revealed an exceptionally long ceramic history that goes back to around 5000 B.C., before pottery-making began in most other parts of the Americas.

Very little is known about the ceramics of Esmeraldas, the northernmost province, except by analogy with southern types. This outstanding mask is related by the stylization of the features to the Chone style, but the frame of flame-like reliefs is without parallel. The mask was made by pressing clay into a mold, a common technique used elsewhere in later times. Though the pigments with which it was painted after firing have washed away, the colors in use were black, white, vermillion, yellow, and sky blue.

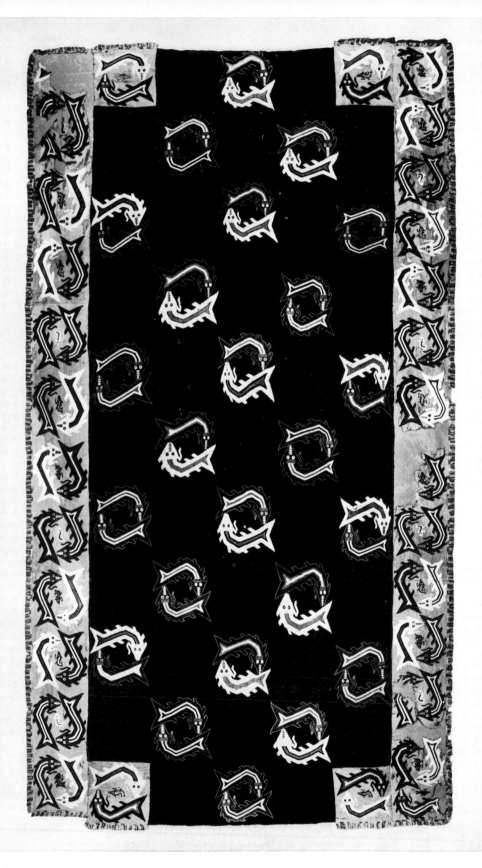

Embroidered Mantle

South coast of Peru, Paracas Necropolis
Wool
Alfred W. Jenkins Fund

Late 1st century B.C. -
early 1st century A.D.
63 by 119 in.
(160 by 302 cm)
34.1560

The Paracas people embroidered large textiles with designs of astonishing richness and intricacy. This famous mantle required over half
a million stitches to complete although less than half the dark blue
center panel is covered by the embroidery. Fine alpaca wool was
used: rich red, which fills the background of the border, golden
yellow, dark green, and blue.

The decoration represents pairs of killer whales, shown swirling
around one another. Each animal is provided with a human arm and
hand. In other Paracas representations the hand holds a sharp flint
knife which may have symbolized the ferocious attack of these sea
animals.

For important burials, the body was bound with many yards of cotton cloth into a huge bundle that enclosed rich woolen mantles and other grave offerings. The garments preserved in such bundles sometimes include matching sets, and this mantle indeed has a short, deeply-fringed shirt with identical embroidery in smaller scale.

239

The Paracas Textile

Cabeza Larga, south coast of Peru,
Paracas Necropolis
Cotton with wool decoration
John T. Underwood Memorial Fund

Late 1st century B. C. -
early 1st century A. D.
65 by 20 in.
(165 by 50.5 cm)
38.121

Needlework of almost incredible fineness and complexity gave this fragile masterpiece the title under which it was first shown and written about in Peru, France, and this country. In the Brooklyn collection of Paracas textiles, one of the world's best, it still stands out, unequaled except for a smaller shawl now in Sweden made entirely of openwork embroidery.

The central field, of loosely woven cotton, is patterned with stylized faces in shades of fine wool yarn that was wrapped about the warps before weaving.

The multicolored woolen border, double-faced like the field, is a procession of minute three-dimensional figures that originally numbered nearly 100. They were worked with a needle in a loop stitch that resembles the finest of knitting. Real and mythological creatures

240

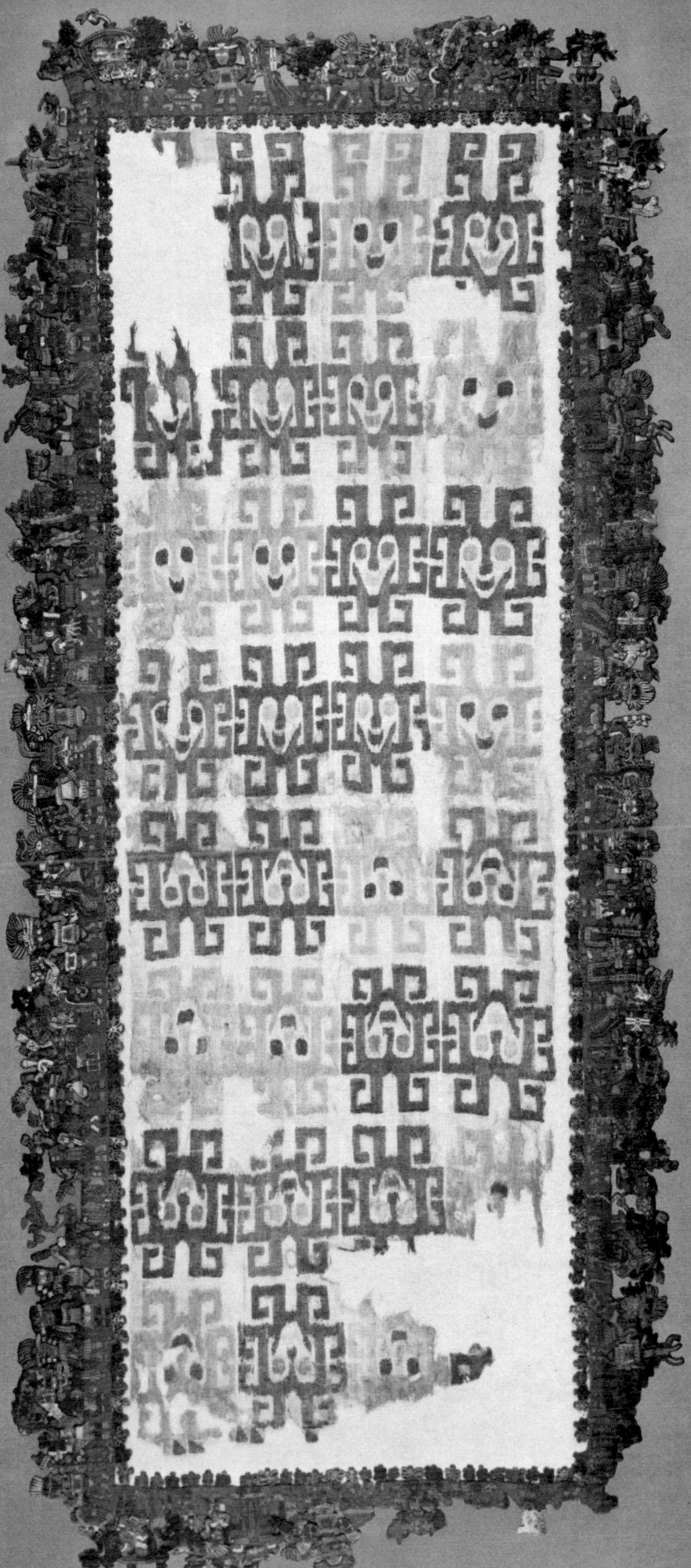

like those later painted on Nazca pottery crowd upon one another carrying weapons, trophy heads, serpents, figures smaller than themselves, and all manner of vegetables and fruits.

As extraordinary as the craftsmanship of the textile is the good fortune that preserved it beneath the windblown sand, to be admired again after two millennia.

244

Funerary Mask

South coast of Peru, Paracas Cavernas
Pottery
Frank L. Babbott and
Dick S. Ramsay Funds

Late 1st century B.C. -
early 1st century A.D.
H. 11⅛ in. (28.4 cm)
64.94

This mask, one of a unique pair, was made for attachment to a mummy bundle. The wide-eyed face with its long projecting nose is crossed by four double-headed serpents whose heads form projecting tabs. From the top rises the head of a human figure. Its face, with a correspondingly large nose, is a repetition, in miniature, of the mask. This figure probably represents a masked impersonator of the same deity. The exact meaning of these symbols is unknown, although it has been suggested that the mask and its companion (L 64.15) may be sun and moon representations.

The mask itself is actually the bottom of an ordinary bowl, pierced for eyes which are inverted clay cones. The design was incised in the fresh clay and, when dry, the mask was fired. The enamel-like paints were a specialty of the Paracas ceramists; they are mixtures, somewhat like sealing wax, of various pigments and resins, which were fused to the pottery surface. The impressions of the mummy wrappings are clearly visible in the enameled tip of the nose.

Stirrup Spout Jar

North coast of Peru, Mochica IV   A. D. 300-550
Pottery, painted brownish red on cream slip   H. 11⅜ in. (29 cm)
Gift from the Eugene Schaefer Collection   36.328

Ceramics of northern Peru show little of the interest in color that is so evident in the south, where the introduction of fired paints at the beginning of the Nazca period led to polychrome pottery with as many as twelve colors. Mochica potters instead adopted only red and cream, using them to make elaborately modeled vessels more realistic and to enhance plainer ones with crisply painted symbolic figures and scenes. Mochica vase painting recalls that of Greece in its self-imposed limitation to two colors and to traditional vessel shapes.

The mythological figures on this jar are shown seated — an unusual pose — talking with evident animation. The one on the right, though unarmed, has the attributes of the hawk warriors, probably a real military order. His companion's headdress marks him as one of the special runners who carried messages of military or supernatural import.

The stirrup spout jar, though difficult to construct and breakable, provided its own handle and was easily carried on the belt. It remained a favorite North Coast form for some twenty-five centuries. Proportions as well as decoration identify this handsome vessel as a product of late Mochica times when painting was at its peak.

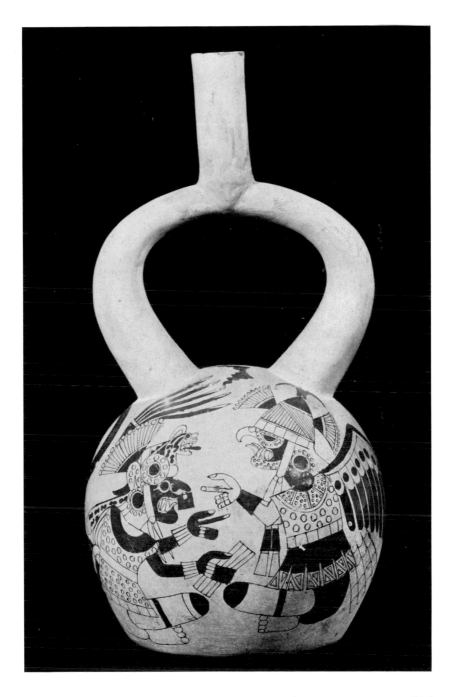

247

Feathered Hat

South or central coast of Peru,   A. D. 600-1000
Wari or Coast Tiahuanaco   H. 6¾ in. (17 cm)
Feathers on a framework of cane, fiber,   41.228
and cotton cloth
A. Augustus Healy Fund

This hat is one of the finest examples that survive of an art form which was brought to a high degree of perfection by ancient Peruvian and Mesoamerican craftsmen. Varicolored feathers — white, yellow, iridescent blue and green, violet, and coral or faded red — formed the mosaic-like decoration. Some are from birds now extinct on the Peruvian coast, and others may have been obtained by trade from the forests on the other side of the Andes. The feathers were glued to thin bark or fiber cloth and then cut very precisely into the required shapes, somewhat like paper cutouts. These in turn were glued onto the fiber cloth stretched over the framework of the hat. The cloth band at the bottom was covered with blue feathers.

Each side is divided into four squares, two of which are filled with geometric patterns, and the other two with crested jaguar heads. The top is divided into triangular quarters.

The style of the hat derives from Wari (Huari), the highland center from which the Peruvian version of the classic Tiahuanaco style spread, possibly through textile trade as well as by conquest.

248

249

Carved Club Head

Marquesas Islands, Polynesia

Wood

Gift of Appleton Sturgis

Late 19th century

H. (of head) 10⅝ in. (27.2 cm)

35.2183

European navigators, who began exploring the vast expanse of the Pacific in the late fifteenth century, never found an island of any consequence uninhabited. Already well established were a variety of agricultural peoples, some of whose forebears probably started out into the island world from continental Asia during the third millennium B.C. In the Marquesas, more than 7,000 miles out, excavated pottery has been dated, through association with radiocarbon techniques, to the late second century B.C.

By historic times, pottery was no longer made in most of Polynesia, the immense triangle marked out by Hawaii at the north, New Zealand at the southwest, and Easter Island. The outlying Marquesas group developed a distinctive sculptural style in wood and also in stone. Monumental figures show the same conventionalizations of the human face as the delicately incised tortoise-shell plaques used in diadems. Tools and weapons, highly valued by the Marquesans — a tribe of warriors — were similarly decorated. The most spectacular are the dark-stained wooden clubs like the one illustrated here which is nearly six feet long. Concave, hooded faces are suggested on each side of the massive, striking head by eyes formed of tiny faces set in rayed disks. Another represents the tip of the nose, while different stylizations of the face are incised above and below.

Door Lintel

New Zealand, Polynesia, Maori
Wood
Frank L. Babbott and
Carll H. De Silver Funds

Late 19th century
H. 13¾ in. (35 cm)
61.126

Carefully preserved oral histories of the Maori tell of two-thousand-mile journeys in great outrigger canoes or double boats between the islands of Central Polynesia and New Zealand. Noble families, like Mayflower descendants, trace their ancestry to the earlier voyagers, who began to arrive about the year 900. A distinctive art style evolved that nevertheless recalls their traditional origins. It displays great technical virtuosity in carving wood, ivory, native nephrite and other stones, and in twined weaving.

Well adapted to the colder climate of New Zealand, village ceremonial houses were substantial, gabled buildings, handsomely ornamented inside and out with panels of carved wood. This fine lintel illustrates the characteristic interlaced composition, enlivened by openwork and the use of different planes of carving. At each end is the *manaia* motif, which resembles a bird in profile with a pretzel-like beak. The human figure at the center has incised spirals that mark important joints of the body, and gleaming eyes that are disks of green South Pacific *Haliotis* shell fitted over wooden pegs that form the pupils.

253

Sculptured Doorpost

New Caledonia, Melanesia　　　　　　Mid- or late 19th century
Painted wood　　　　　　　　　　　　H. 62½ in. (159 cm)
Anonymous Gift　　　　　　　　　　　52.124

Melanesia comprises the countless islands and groups that stretch from Indonesia across the South Pacific above Australia as far eastward as Fiji. In this tropical oceanic world the violence of nature seems to have generated an especially dramatic quality in the art produced by its people. Architectural decoration and ceremonial paraphernalia were dedicated to ancestral spirits and deities representing the forces of nature.

Until European influence and mutual hostility destroyed native culture in the nineteenth century, important houses on the island of New Caledonia presented a unique and impressive architectural style. They were circular in plan, with thatched walls and conical roofs topped by spire-like carvings. Sculpture on the structural parts of the building symbolized the presence of powerful ancestors and gave them a place of residence in it. The largest members were the doorposts, made from single planks or sections of great tree trunks. Strong, forbidding faces stared outward above the areas patterned with concentric lozenges. They were painted black, with red added in the geometric part. Since the house was customarily destroyed when the head of the family died, few undamaged architectural sculptures remain.

Ceremonial Shield

Guadalcanal, Solomon Islands
Painted basketry with
mother-of-pearl inlay
Frank L. Babbott and
Carll H. De Silver Funds

Mid-19th century
H. 32⅝ in. (83 cm)
59.63

Native culture had largely lost its identity in the Solomon Islands
before the bitter struggle of the war in the Pacific brought the attention of the world to focus there. At the time when traditional arts
were still vigorous, a number of styles and special techniques distinguished different parts of the long archipelago. In the west, handsomely carved figures and paddles enhanced large canoes for head-
hunting expeditions. The central islands produced the only stone
sculpture in Melanesia and certain openwork pendants cut from the
heavy shell of *tridaena*, the giant clam.

Inlaying with mother-of-pearl, the most notable art of the Solo-
mons, was not developed to the same degree anywhere else. Small
units cut into a few standardized, fancy shapes were usually set in
rows to decorate wooden figures or vessels. On this gleaming ceremonial shield they form the principal design. It stands out with
great elegance against areas filled with the lacquer-like black and
brick-red paint that covers the basketry foundation. Comparatively
few other shields of this kind are known. They are so alike that they
must all have come from the same place of manufacture, thought to
be Guadalcanal. This one, collected in 1852, is in unusually fine
condition.

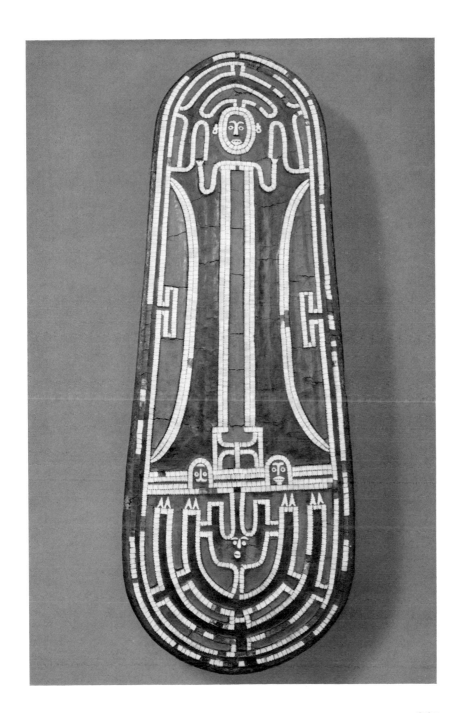

Malangan Mask

New Ireland, Melanesia
Wood and fiber

Late 19th century
H. 16¼ in. (41 cm)
01.180

The preoccupation with ancestral spirits and genealogy, which gave rise to so many Pacific art forms, found its most elaborate expression in the *Malangan* ceremonies of New Ireland, an island in the Bismarck Archipelago north of New Guinea. Clans competed with each other in presenting prolonged and spectacular memorial festivals dedicated to legendary ancestors and important members of the family, recent and long dead. In preparation, the clan employed artists who worked in secret to carve and paint ceremonial equipment and decorations appropriate to the occasion. The free-standing figures, masks, and wall panels are complex symbolic compositions emphasizing openwork and intricate surface patterns.

Masks such as this simulate the traditional coiffure of male mourners who shaved away their hair, leaving only a central crest. The mask is constructed of wood and several kinds of fiber in warm brown and yellow tones, enlivened with white, black, red, and yellow. Like most New Ireland figure sculptures, it has eye sockets set with gleaming green cat's eyes, the opercula of the Pacific turban shell.

Canoe Prow

Sepik River, New Guinea, Melanesia   Early 20th century
Wood   L. 33½ in. (85 cm)
Gift in memory of Abraham Barstok and   62.54
Frank L. Babbott Fund

The island of New Guinea, 1,300 miles long, adjoins Indonesia, Australia, and the rest of western Melanesia. Long subject to European influences and inhabited by native peoples of three major racial groups, it developed several regional styles. The large Sepik River region on the north coast presents a rich variety of sub-styles which were further diversified by intertribal trade and copying. With the disintegration of ceremonial life, sculpture has lost much of the meaning that gave it force, and craftsmanship has begun to decline.

At its best, Sepik sculpture is notable for the dramatic impact of its stylized human and animal figures which represent supernatural beings. Several forms may be combined, as in this striking canoe prow. Seen from above it appears as a huge mask with flaring cut-out nostrils and mouth and a bird-like helmet. A small figure, now headless, is superimposed at the chin. From the side, it suggests the head of the crocodile, which is portrayed more literally on certain other canoes. Though painted originally, the wood is now split and stained and has a weatherbeaten, grey surface that emphasizes the monumentality of the sculpture.

Scare-devil

Nicobar Islands   19th century
Wood   H. 28¼ in. (72 cm)
The Woodward Memorial Funds   63.57

Although the Nicobar archipelago lies near the western entrance to the Strait of Malacca, the principal trade route to the East Indies, native culture remained comparatively unaffected by passing trade vessels, Oriental or Western. The only art recorded was wood sculpture, in the form of *hanta koi*, or "scare-devils," intended to keep threatening, malevolent spirits at bay. The ones seen in coastal villages were mythological creatures and figures in European dress, which were probably of a later style. Early drawings after these objects and the few examples preserved in collections show that they were generally composed of several separately carved parts.

Only two others are known of this type, characterized as a heavy-bodied crouching figure with a turtle carapace on the back. Its extraordinarily long arms, set in sockets, stretch forward horizontally. The eyes are pointed ovals of shell, and the mouth, with its characteristic square-cut teeth, was painted red. The figure wears a chin-strap helmet, pointed at the top in the Malayan manner. It suggests that the style derives from some part of the Malay Peninsula where related dialects are spoken, though local tradition says that the original inhabitants came down from Burma.

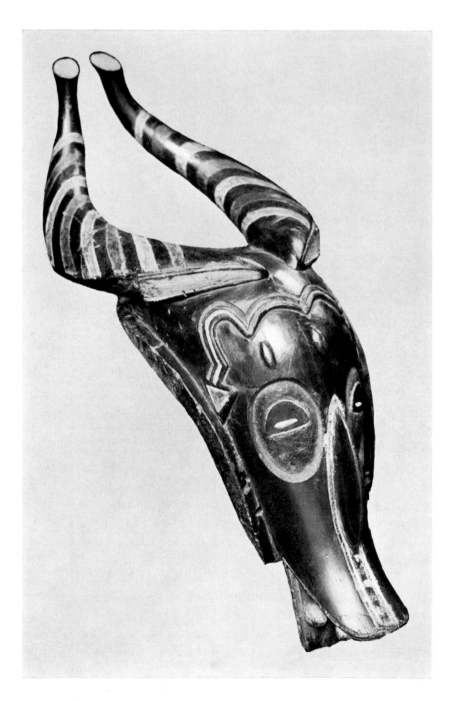

266

Antelope Dance Mask

Ivory Coast, Africa, Guro
Painted wood
Museum Expedition

Early 20th century
H. 21¼ in. (54 cm)
22.756

The Brooklyn Museum was the first in this country to remove the art of Africa from the ethnology halls where, as noted in the 1923 catalogue, the "artistic significance is obscured by the wealth of material, and ... lost in the efforts made for its elucidation." The first installation included fabrics, fashion designs, and furniture inspired by the 1,454 African objects gathered by the farsighted Steward Culin, who amassed so many of the treasures in our collection.

Among these legacies is the universally appealing Guro antelope mask. Age contributes to its effect of dark, gleaming elegance set off by light-colored details. Though its flowing curves may, at some points in the cycle of taste, appear over-refined, they convey with clarity the same force of nature that other African styles express in a different idiom. The mask was worn in agricultural fertility ceremonies of the *Zamle* secret society.

267

Nimba Mask

Guinea, Africa, Baga
Wood
A. Augustus Healy and
Ella C. Woodward Funds

Early 20th century
H. 47¼ in. (120 cm)
57.19

In most African sculpture, supernatural beings are conceived as having human, rather than animal, form. Emphatic stylization brings out their superhuman quality. Nowhere is this means used more effectively than by sculptors of the Baga tribe who carve forceful male and female standing figures, tables with Atlantean supports, and perhaps the most striking of all African masks.

The massive *Nimba* mask appears in dances performed by the *Simo* secret society after the harvest of rice, the staple crop. It towers above the head of the dancer carrying it, who is enveloped entirely by a palm-fiber robe draped about the wooden shoulders and under the arching breasts, hiding the handles as well as the dancer.

The severity of the strong, simple forms and proud set of the head is relieved by surface patterns that reveal Moslem influence in the northern Sudan region from which the Baga came to the coast.

Flute Player

Benin City, Nigeria, Africa   A. D. 1500-1700
Cast brass   H. 23½ in. (59.5 cm)
Gift of Mr. and Mrs. Alastair B. Martin   55.87

Benin bronzes and ivory sculptures, spanning a period of at least five
centuries, are a reminder of the long, artistic traditions that survive
only in the contemporary art of peoples who used perishable materials. Certain Benin sculptures can be dated in the sixteenth century
by the Portuguese costumes depicted in works like the well-known
wall plaque in the Brooklyn Museum collection. Benin oral tradition
places the introduction of metalworking in the year 1280.

The art of Benin became an instant sensation in 1897, on the return
of a British expeditionary force sent to restore order after the ex-
termination of a diplomatic trade mission. Among their treasures
were the masterfully cast bronzes retired to storage in the eighteenth
century from the royal palace, the source to which this splendid
sculpture, and many others in the world's museums, can be traced.

Working exclusively for the court and its elaborate ancestor cult,
the royal artisans maintained an appropriately decorative, naturalistic
style.

The hollow figure was cast by the lost-wax method in an alloy that
is a type of brass, rather than bronze. A special refinement was to
enliven the eyes with pupils of iron, set in the wax model before
casting. The guilloche-bordering of the kilt was cast, but the other
patterns of Moorish derivation were added by chasing.

Door from a War Chief's House

Nigeria, Africa, Yoruba
Wood
Museum Expedition

Early 20th century
H. 48 in. (121.5 cm)
22.1526

Just east of the old Kingdom of Benin, the Yoruba peoples preserve in wood a vigorous style that reflects Benin influence and the common derivation of both traditions from ancient Ife, a Yoruba city. Sculpture continues to be in demand for secular purposes and to serve the needs of some four hundred cults.

Certain masters developed individual styles, and their work is recognized in Yorubaland and abroad. The relief carving on the door illustrated, part of the original Culin collection, is from the same hand as a somewhat larger door now in Berlin.

The composition, which has an almost Gothic flavor, glorifies the war leader or *Balogan*. He is shown mounted, a frequent theme in Yoruba sculpture in the round. With him are his attendants and staffbearer, a row of warriors armed with rifles, and his wives and children. The women's headdresses and the differing facial scarifications indicate the complexity and importance of tribal affiliation.

273

Mortuary Figure

Gabon, Africa, Fang
Wood
Frank L. Babbott Fund

Early 20th century
H. 23 in. (58.5 cm)
51.3

Widely dispersed through the deeply forested region of northern Gabon, the Fang have now lost the force and homogeneity that vitalized their sculpture. They no longer carve the fine masks and figures that first brought attention to African art in general.

Ancestors were held in reverence by the Fang, and custom required a carved figure or head to be set on the bark container in which the skulls of important forebears were preserved. In recent times they served more as guardians than memorials. They lack any mark of individuality or portraiture but express a generalized protective power.

The elegance and self-contained dignity of this much-admired figure are heightened by the fine unadorned finish, the symmetry, and the interpretation of different parts of the body as geometric units.

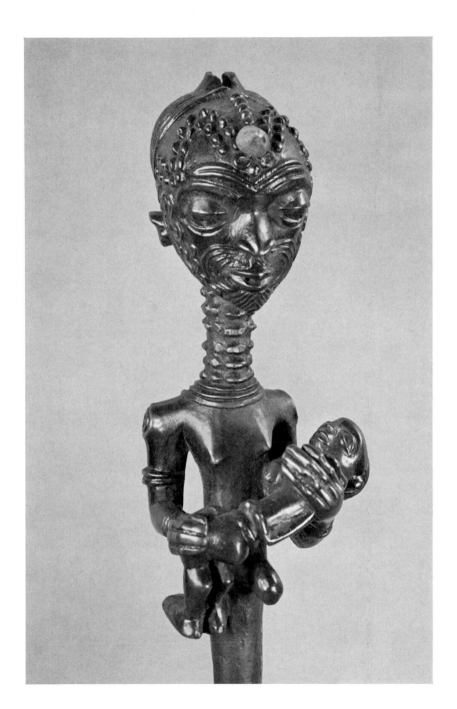

Staff Head

Central Congo, Africa, Bena Lulua   19th century
Wood   H. 14 in. (35.6 cm)
Frank S. Benson Fund   50.124

The Bena Lulua, a Baluba tribe of the central Congo, are noted for
expressively stylized standing male and female figures some of which
are only six inches tall. Despite their small size, they project a tense
vitality. This mother and child group is an exceptionally fine example
and exhibits the characteristics of the Bena Lulua style: the figure is
elongated with an especially attenuated neck, a large, distinctively
shaped head, and huge half-closed eyes. Bena Lulua artists exaggerat-
ed the elaborate facial and body scarification, which is no longer
practiced today, to create strong relief patterns.

The lower part of the woman's body is not defined, but simply
thinned further to a rod or handle. Its use, and that of other Bena
Lulua carvings, is uncertain. They may have been fetishes or com-
memorative figures.

Royal Portrait of Bom Bosh

Central Congo, Africa, Bushongo (Bakuba)   18th century
Wood   H. 19½ in. (49.4 cm)
Gift of Mr. and Mrs. Robert E. Blum,   61.33
     Mr. and Mrs. Alastair B. Martin, and
     Mr. and Mrs. Donald M. Oenslager;
     Mrs. Florence E. Blum Fund

The cultured Bushongo nation was the counterpart of the West-African kingdoms of Ife and Benin and maintained its ancient theocratic supremacy in the central Congo until the end of the last century. A long oral history sets forth the deeds of kings. It records that the tradition of royal portraiture was begun by the 93rd king, whose portrait is now in the British Museum. Bom Bosh, the 96th, reigned in the mid-seventeenth century. These two early figures may not have been carved from life: they differ very little in style or costume from those of three late eighteenth-century rulers.

The royal portraits, like Egyptian hieratic sculptures, are highly conventionalized. Each king is seated on a square platform, which repeats the shape and surface pattern of his headdress and contrasts pleasingly with the rounded contours of the figure. He holds the symbol of office, a throwing knife called *shongo,* which gave the Bushongo the name that distinguishes them from other Bakuba peoples. Individual kings are differentiated by emblematic objects in front of them. A drum with a severed hand in relief identifies Bom Bosh who is remembered as a great warrior.

Decorative Arts

Buffet

Dijon, France
Walnut
Gift of Mrs. J. Fuller Feder

About 1600
H. 102 in. (259 cm)
54.75

Classical architectural ornamentation for furniture was introduced in Europe with the advent of the Renaissance. The elaborate carving on this buffet is reminiscent of designs published in 1572 by Hugues Sambin, a cabinetmaker in Dijon. These designs are, in fact, a translation of Italian classical motifs into a French version that suited the taste of the court of Francis I, who had brought Italian artists, such as Leonardo da Vinci and Primaticcio, to France. The overall pattern on the front of this piece and the way the structural aspects of column and lintel are minimized are characteristics in keeping with the stylistic period of Mannerism during which the preference for a "horror vacui" made architects cover their façades with closely spaced ornamentation.

Embroidery

England
Linen
Henry W. Healy Fund

About 1625
Complete piece 47⅝ by 14¾ in.
(121 by 37.5 cm)
32.476-4

Examples of the type of embroidery illustrated, part of an early seventeenth-century bed valance, are rare. This one was formerly in the collection of the noted English needlewoman and author, Mary Symonds (Mrs Guy Antrobus).

The valance combines both plain embroidery and knotted thread-work — a lost art, in which the threads were knotted by means of a shuttle-like instrument, the navette — then sewn down to the ground cloth. The technique was used both in silk and linen threads.

This work is done in cream linen on a light brown linen ground, said to be the original. A darker brown fabric underlies some of the floral petals and leaves.

Armoire

Peru

Walnut

A. Augustus Healy Fund and others

About 1650

H. 94 in. (239 cm)

48.206.1

Peruvian craftsmen exploited the flamboyance of the Baroque in the lavishly carved furniture they produced in the seventeenth century. This three-part armoire is characteristic of their best work. The decorative details such as the scroll, the rosette, and the lion feet, represent familiar borrowings from Spain. Only here they are simplified and flattened and thus appear bold and primitive, suggesting the influence of the indigenous people who, by the seventeenth century, were making their mark in the crafts. This Indian influence is particularly noteworthy in textile designs where traditional Indian motifs were incorporated in examples based on European models.

Goblet

England   1680 - 1690
Glass   H. 18 in. (45.7 cm)
Special Subscription and Collection Fund   13.706

This is a particularly rare example of late seventeenth-century English glass. The richness of the applied decoration and its regal size suggest that it may have been an important presentation piece. The lead glass can readily be identified as English and is either the work of the London glasshouse founded by George Ravenscroft, or a slightly later product of one of his followers.

Ravenscroft, originally a dealer who sold glass manufactured in Venice, was responsible for the development of clear lead "crystal" in 1676. Working at the Savoy Glasshouse from 1673, his innovations included discovering a way of using English raw materials instead of the Venetian imports to which his forerunners had been restricted. The translation of Neri's *L'Arte Vetraria* by Dr. Christopher Merret made new information available to Ravenscroft to facilitate his research and experimentation and probably was an important reason for his success. The glass he perfected is seen at its best in heavier and simpler forms than the soda lime glass that was made in Italy; gradually the influence of Venetian design, which was best suited to very thin flexible glass, diminished, and an English style developed.

The early lead glass from the Savoy Glasshouse was often crizzled because of excessive alkali in the glass composition; when the formula had been improved a glass seal was often applied to the work. This goblet does not bear the seal and is likely to be by a Ravenscroft follower working in the 1680's.

North Room of the Jan Martense Schenck House

Flatlands (Brooklyn), New York
Gift of The Avalon Foundation
and an Anonymous Fund

About 1675
20 by 20 feet (6 by 6 m)

The Jan Martense Schenck House is an important example of seventeenth-century New York architecture reflecting the Dutch tradition. It has been reconstructed at the Museum in its original size, a simple two-room structure. Depicted here is the parlor-bedroom. The heavy ceiling beams braced at either end illustrate a type known particularly in The Netherlands and used by Dutch settlers in the New World until the early 1730's. The open hearth is also typical of seventeenth-century Dutch homes in the Old and New World. Carpets often served as table and chest covers in early interiors because they were too precious to be put on the floor. The chairs around the table are upholstered in a knotted fabric called "Turkey work." The ceramics are Dutch Delft, the tin-glaze earthenware popular in the seventeenth and early eighteenth centuries. The bed, enclosed by panelling and curtains, is in the left corner.

291

Tankard

Jacob Boelen (New York, 1657-1729)   About 1685
Mark: I B twice   H. 7⅛ in. (20 cm)
Silver   26.60
Gift of Mrs. Richard van Wyck
and Mrs. Henry de Bevoise Schenck
in Memory of Richard van Wyck

Silver played an important role on the American scene from the middle of the seventeenth century on. Having silver coin fashioned into objects was a method of making it more readily identifiable and, therefore, more secure before the advent of banks in the American colonies. The silversmith combined the function of artisan with that of banker since he dealt in a commodity that was in essence capital, and since the technique he used involved the relatively rare use of molds, he was able to keep up with the latest fashion when he so desired. American silversmiths varied in style, as did their clients, and the range from the most conservative to the most fashionable, as well as from the most simple to the most elaborate, is broad. Albeit, there is the same directness in American silver design as in design of other media. Forms were developed to suit the different tastes discerned in the various communities along the Atlantic seaboard during the seventeenth and eighteenth centuries.

New York tankards demonstrate how several old-world influences were combined when cultures merged. In New York, where Dutch burghers lived under English rule after 1664, Dutch and English decorative concepts were often combined. In this tankard, the straight, tapering sides and flat cover are characteristically English;

from The Netherlands came the idea of decorating the base with a cut-leaf motif. The squat, heavy proportions, the cast cocoon-shaped thumb piece at the top, and the cupid head end of the handle are elements typical of the work of New York craftsmen who, synthesizing various influences, created a homogeneous style clearly American in character.

Chair Seat

England or Holland

Wool

The Henry W. Healy Fund

About 1688

17⅝ by 21½ in. (44.2 by 53.5 cm)

32.476-2

Crewel work, — the art of embroidering with loosely twisted wool yarns or "crewels" — rose to popularity in England in the seventeenth century and continued in this country through the eighteenth.

Typical of crewel work are the extravagant designs — the luxuriant foliage with fantastic fruits and flowers or exotic birds and beasts. Many of the motifs may be traced to Elizabethan embroideries. Some have a decidedly Oriental feeling.

The chair seat illustrated was obtained by the Museum from Mrs. Guy Antrobus. It is documented as having been made in Holland for Richard San(d)ford of Nynehead Court, Wiltshire, England, on the occasion of his wedding. The entire suite of embroideries consisted of bed furniture, including hangings, canopy, valances, bedback, and quilt for a four-post bedstead, as well as pairs of curtains for five windows and covers for twelve chairs.

295

Salt

Jacobus Vander Spiegel
(New York, 1668-1708)
Mark: ISV in trefoil
Silver
H. Randolph Lever Fund

About 1690
H. 3¼ in. (8.2 cm)
65.5

This spool-shaped salt is an extraordinary piece of New York silver: it is the single known example of a Dutch-style standing salt made in America. Said to have come down in the Westervelt family, who settled in Flatlands, now a part of Brooklyn, in the seventeenth century, it bears the mark of Jacobus Vander Spiegel, a silversmith active in New York from 1685 to 1705. Spool-shaped salts are generally larger than the Vander Spiegel version but the small size is encountered in Dutch silver after 1675 at about the time the trencher salt, the purely functional round or oval form made from mediaeval times to the seventeenth century in wood and pewter, was first produced in silver.

Jacobus Vander Spiegel was one of New York's outstanding silversmiths at the end of the seventeenth century. Less than twenty pieces bearing his mark have survived, but this small group of identified examples reveals his skill and sophistication. Along with his New York competitors, Vander Spiegel usually followed the practice of combining Dutch and English design elements to create a style that was distinctive for New York. In this salt he stayed surprisingly close to the Dutch prototype.

296

Tea Caddy

Delft, Holland
Mark: IDP/1698
Tin-glazed earthenware
Anonymous Fund

H. 6⅝ in. (16.8 cm)
64.3.4

Delft's transition from a center of beer production to one of pottery took place in the seventeenth century when, because of a decline in the popularity of the breweries which had been Delft's major industry, it was decided that the stills should be remodelled into kilns and that the capital available should be used to develop a trade in the new product. However unrelated beer and pottery may be, the townsmen of Delft were correct in appraising the market, and the new product was very successful. The ceramic-ware known as Delft is a tin-glazed earthenware, the colors and designs of which were inspired mainly by Chinese and Near Eastern porcelain. A development from majolica, delftware differed from its Oriental models in being of a heavier ceramic body, a fact that brought about a boldness in design consistent with middle-class Western taste of the time.

This tea caddy is in a shape that was adapted from the more usual metal caddies of the period. The decoration is a good example of how the Delft decorator might combine the Oriental color scheme, blue and white, and Western subject matter. The symbolic figures in the niches on the sides are of classical inspiration while the view of a couple drinking tea fits into the category of genre scenes, a subject of special interest to Dutch artists of the seventeenth century.

Rabat

Flanders

Point d'Angleterre

Ella C. Woodward Fund

Early 18th century

13⅜ by 13 in. (34 by 33 cm)

31.778

The demand for lace, limited by law and by cost to the nobility and wealthy few, reached its peak in the eighteenth century — and always exceeded the supply. Countries vied for the trade. Colbert, the astute Minister of Finance of Louis XIV, imported lace-workers from Venice to establish the industry in France. The "Points de France" soon equalled the exquisite needle-made laces of Venice.

Flanders led in the art of bobbin lace-making of which this rabat, or gentleman's cravat of Point d'Angleterre, is an outstanding example. The various motifs were made separately, then assembled and "grounded" by net or mesh.

The design of the rabat is typical of a "gentleman's lace" — a hunting scene worked in relief, with the main figures outlined in a raised cordonnet.

Panel

Russia   18th century
Embroidered net   29 by 78¾ in. (73.7 by 200 cm)
Gift of Mrs. Edward S. Harkness   31.345

The embroidered net panel, edge of a bed sheet, is from the noted collection of Russian textiles, costumes, and folk art gathered over a period of fifty years by the Countess de Shabelsky.

The various motifs are embroidered in white on a white, hand-made, square mesh ground in linen thread. The border is bobbin lace.

Decorative bed coverings, curtains, and towels figured prominently in the peasant home. Young brides were expected to present each of their wedding guests with something of their own making, and this is the type of work usually given. The towels or scarves were used ceremonially; in the home, they were hung over mirrors or icons.

Some of the designs are landscapes, as in the panel illustrated; others are floral, geometric, or they include animal and bird motifs. They fall largely into three groups: white on white embroideries, pastel-colored laces, and red and blue — or simply red — embroidery on natural linen. On festive occasions such as weddings or feast days, they were used to decorate sledges or wagons.

Robe à la Française

Probably Norway   18th century
Embroidered gold silk   H. 57 in. (149 cm)
Ella C. Woodward Fund   30.955

This gown was purchased in Scandinavia thirty-six years ago. The loose-flowing back, falling from box pleats set at the neckline, identifies it as a "robe à la française," — a mode which was fashionable during the better part of the eighteenth century. This mode is often associated today with Watteau, whose paintings provide many illustrations of this style.

The similarity of the embroidery pattern to a brocaded textile from this Museum's collections is striking. The brocade was woven in Spitalfields, England, about 1750. It is not unusual to find embroidery design derived from fabrics, and it is possible that the design for the costume, although presumably Norwegian work, was drawn from the woven material. Some of the detached floral sprays are appliqued in pastel silks, then outlined in satin stitch. Shadings are subtly done, and the motifs gracefully arranged on the gold ground. The lace ruffles at neck and sleeve are Point d'Argentan, a recent addition although of the period.

305

306

Table

New York or New Jersey
Cherry wood
Gift of Jerome Blum

About 1690
H. 27 in. (68.6 cm)
64.201

American furniture tends to be simple and forthright in design, with modifications from the Old World models to enable the craftsman to avoid complexities beyond his abilities. While in provincial English furniture there are often misunderstood or badly executed details, in American work the design is changed to suit the skill of the maker. Working within their limitations, American cabinetmakers developed local styles which reflected the taste of specific areas.

In contrast to the lightness preferred in New England, this example, with two boldly turned legs connected by low stretchers, is typical of the style favored in New York and New Jersey; in addition, cherry wood was used in the Hudson River Valley extensively. A table with a top that folded down was very practical during this period when the number of rooms in a house was limited, and each room had to be used for sleeping, working, eating, and entertaining.

High Chest

New England

Walnut veneer

Dick S. Ramsay Fund

1680-1710

H. 61 in. (154.9 cm)

58.35

The high chest is a storage piece introduced in England early in the
seventeenth century and in America towards the end of that century.
The form evolved from the more decorative jewel or treasure chests
on stands that had come into fashion in Italy in the sixteenth century
and it highlights the change from "joinery" or carpentry to cabinet-
making in furniture. Earlier, oak had been the favored wood, and
furniture construction, not differing from housebuilding to any great
degree, was bold and gross.

This high chest is one expression of the new style, called the
William and Mary style by students of the history of American furniture, in which details were handled with greater delicacy, and new
skills were exhibited by the craftsman. Elaborate veneer — here, the
burl of the walnut tree — applied to the carcase of the chest to create
a vibrant surface, and the delicately turned legs and flat curving
stretchers are visible details that are a result of the new technique.
The use of dovetailing in the construction of the drawers and the
method of screwing the legs and putting the stretchers together are
additional characteristics of the new approach.

The proportions and the relation to documented pieces suggest that
this chest should be attributed to New England. Introduced as one
of a number of new forms and made more elaborately than earlier
examples, the high chest marks the beginning of greater elegance
and sophistication in American craftsmanship.

Chest-on-Frame

New England   About 1680
Oak and pine   H. 35 in. (88.9 cm)
Gift of Mrs. William Sterling Peters   49.190.1

This small chest is made of oak in the earliest tradition of American furniture, but the turned legs and the painted panels on the front are two elements of the design which relate to more advanced stylistic developments. The legs are simplifications of the columnar shapes used in elegant European furniture. The front panels are painted red and embellished with flowering trees in imitation of Oriental lacquer favored as an exotic complement in many Western interiors. Instead of applying the many layers of varnish colored with pigment as required in the lacquer technique, the Western version, called "japanning," involved paint more often than lacquer. The interest in seeking out Oriental inspiration was popular enough to warrant the publication of a treatise in London in 1688 explaining the process, namely, *The Art of Japanning*, by Stalker and Parker.

The upper section is reached by lifting the lid, and there is a single drawer below which looks like two at first glance. The original function of the piece is not known. It could have been used for the storage of books and papers, or it might have been a washstand with a bowl and water bottle in the upper section.

311

312

Book Box and Chest

Box: New York (?)   About 1675
       Pine   H. 9 in. (22.9 cm)
       Woodward Memorial Fund   24.436

Chest: Hadley, Massachusetts   1706
       Oak   H. 23¼ in. (59.1 cm)
       Henry L. Batterman Fund   14.707

Two varieties of carving known in American furniture of the seventeenth century are represented in the pieces illustrated. The pine slant-top box resting on the chest is carved in geometric patterns in comparatively high relief related particularly to the Dutch settlers in the New World. This kind of work is called "Friesland Carving." The basic motif is the classical rosette which has been stylized radically to suit the abilities of the craftsmen involved.

The oak chest, on the other hand, has an abstract floral design chipped out in flat silhouette relief. This scheme of simplification is used on a relatively limited number of chests, all made in the area around Hadley, Massachusetts, and called Hadley chests. The initials MS are thought to be for Martha Sheldon whose descendants resided in the Porter house in Wethersfield, Connecticut, from where two of the rooms in the series of American interiors at the Museum come. The carving on the Hadley chest uses the flower-bouquet motif which introduced an exotic note in seventeenth-century design, having derived from the Near Eastern ceramics and textiles imported at the time.

313

Tray

Paul de Lamerie (England, 1688-1751)   About 1720
Mark: PL in script surmounted by a   L. 16½ in. (41.9 cm)
crown/lion passant/crowned leopard   22.1813
Silver
Gift of Rev. Alfred Duane Pell

Paul de Lamerie was one of the great silversmiths to work in England in the eighteenth century. Of Huguenot background, as were so many of the fine craftsmen in England, he produced elaborate pieces in the Baroque and Rococo styles.

This tray, which does not have the date mark ordinarily applied, was probably made in about 1720, before Rococo design influenced de Lamerie. Its style is in the French tradition of silver work which, succeeding the earlier, thin silver elaborately embossed in the Dutch tradition, became dominant in England from the late seventeenth century on.

315

Beaker

Henricus Boelen (New York, 1697-1755) About 1730
Mark: HB H. 6¾ in. (17.2 cm)
Silver 21.236
Gift of Timothy Ingraham Hubbard

This beaker was made as a communion cup for the Dutch Reformed
Church of Flatlands, now a part of Brooklyn. It is in the shape of a
simple drinking vessel, repeating a design well-known in seventeenth-century Dutch examples that were used in New York churches.
The engraving is probably based on a print published in the seventeenth century. The figure represents "Faith" and is accompanied by
"Hope" and "Charity." This group appears also on a number of
earlier New York and Dutch communion beakers. The inscription
in Greek seems to have been copied by an engraver who did not
understand the language.

Henricus Boelen, the son of Jacob Boelen, was active from about
1718 to 1755. He inherited his father's silver business in 1729 and was
responsible for a great variety of fashionable secular silver as well as
conservative ritual forms like this.

316

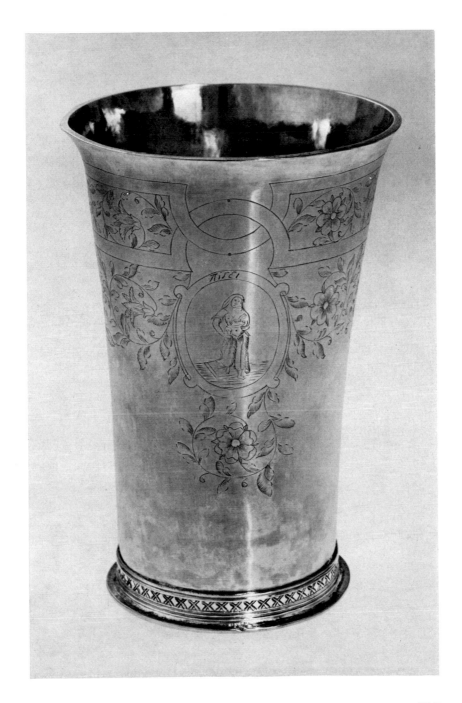

317

318

Bowl

Staffordshire, England
Salt glaze
Gift of Mrs. Robert H. Blum

About 1740
H. 3½ in. (8.9 cm)
D. 6⅛ in. (15.6 cm)
54.3.1

Salt glaze is a thin stoneware covered with a glaze of salt. It was introduced early in the eighteenth century in the Staffordshire region as an inexpensive substitute for porcelain and has the robust charm characteristic of folk art. Requiring lower temperatures than porcelain and being made without kaolin — the rare clay which is the chief ingredient of porcelain — salt glaze was too brittle to be durable. It flourished from about 1720 to 1770 when it was replaced by the sturdier creamware.

The applied relief decoration of ships in a port represents the Battle of Porto Bello and is accompanied by the inscription: "The British Glory Revived by Admiral Vernon. He took Porto Bello with six ships only November 22, 1739." This event in eighteenth-century British history was obviously an important topical subject when the bowl was made. The curving sides of the piece suggest the influence of contemporary importations from the Orient.

Dining Room

Danbury, Connecticut

About 1755
14 by 11 feet
(4.25 by 3.35 m)

Connecticut farmhouses were panelled simply but details often reveal subtle niceties far beyond those found in ordinary houses of a later era. One example of such details in this room is the projection of the cornice above the windows which serves almost as a valance. The ware on the table is pewter which was popular in rural areas in the last quarter of the eighteenth century but gradually was replaced by inexpensive earthenware as represented here by the creamware pitcher and the candlesticks. The conservatism of rural design is seen in the chairs around the table. The Windsor high chair is a type mentioned as early as the 1730's and occurs until the middle of the nineteenth century. The side chairs, with typical Queen Anne-style backs and turned legs joined by stretchers in the William and Mary style, are similar to those shown in a chairmaker's advertisement of the early nineteenth century.

Bed Room, The Reuben Bliss House

Springfield, Massachusetts

About 1754
18 by 14 feet
(5.50 by 4.25 m)

This room is a good example of a typical New England "chamber" of pre-revolutionary days.

From a New England salt box, the central-chimney wooden structure with a sloping addition in the rear, this bedroom is of particular interest because of the panelled ceiling. Although panelled walls had been used in the seventeenth century and were given greater distinction in the eighteenth century by the introduction of decorative schemes in which the wood is divided in moldings that simulate stone, ceilings were most often simply plastered. This one may have been an embellishment the builder used to show his ability in his own home. The first resident of this house was Reuben Bliss, a joiner, or to put it in more modern terminology, a carpenter.

Whether or not the panelling was painted originally is difficult to determine today. No traces of paint remain, but the fact that the panels are made of pine — a soft wood that requires a protective coating — is an indication that the walls were to be painted.

The proportions of the panelling are in harmony with the furniture of the period which is used to furnish the room. The high chest and the side chair were made in neighboring Connecticut in about 1750 and are in the American Queen Anne style. The bed, a simple "pencil post" that probably was made shortly after the Revolution, is hung with English chintz that bears the mark of *I. Jones, 1761*. Red and white printed cotton was very popular for eighteenth-century bedrooms.

322

323

Coffee Pot

Daniel Christian Fueter
(New York, active about 1754-1779)
Mark: DCF in oval and N. YORK
in irregular rectangle
Silver
Bequest of Samuel E. Haslett

About 1765
H. 12³/₁₆ in. (31 cm)
20.796

This type of tall pyriform coffee pot was particularly popular in America between 1770 and 1800. Daniel Christian Fueter, the silversmith responsible for this piece, was active in New York from about 1754 to 1779. Although he was of Swiss origin and had spent some time in London, the work he did in New York was distinctly American, conservative, and relatively simple. Like his American competitors, the quality of the metal Fueter used was fine, and his designs tended to be less ornate than English models. The style of this pot is very similar to that of examples made by the more famous Paul Revere, Myer Myers, and Joseph Richardson.

324

326

Parlor, The Russell House

Providence, Rhode Island   1772
Gift of The Rembrandt Club   14 by 14 feet (4.25 by 4.25 m)

The Joseph Russell House was built by one of the foremost merchants of Providence for his second wife, Amey, foster daughter of Stephen Hopkins, a signer of the Declaration of Independence. The house is a three-story structure, and its handsome architectural detail was inspired by designs in the architectural handbooks published in the eighteenth century to guide gentlemen building homes. Russell may have used two such books, since the front door resembles an illustration in Batty Langley's *The Builder's Compleat Assistant* (London, 1766), and the fireplace and general design of the parlor follow suggestions to be found in *Palladio Londinensis or the London Art of Building* by William Salmon (London, 1748). The proportions of the room also follow the ideas of Salmon who, in attempting to introduce the concepts of the Renaissance to eighteenth-century builders, stressed symmetry and the classical orders.

The furnishings in this room offer the typical contrast between architectural detail and decoration. The classical background was used to set off the more asymmetrical Rococo style popular in furniture. The examples seen here are in American Chippendale which was at the height of fashion in the 1770's.

327

Plaque with Four Muses and Apollo

England
Mark: 2 Wedgwood/& Bentley
Blue and white jasperware
The Emily Winthrop Miles Collection

About 1775
L. 15½ in. (39.4 cm)
59.202.23

Decorative jasperware plaques mark an important moment in the history of English ceramics. They are a part of the "Ornamental"

wares offered by Josiah Wedgwood after about 1770 when he had formed the separate company with Thomas Bentley to make artistic wares; at that time Wedgwood was becoming the largest producer of ceramics in England. Jasperware is a stoneware body developed by him; it is named for a dull quartz that was used in antiquity for small reliefs. Best known in a grey-blue, jasperware was also made in a variety of pale colors.

The personages represented are: Erato, the Muse of Erotic Poetry; Euterpe, the Muse of Lyric Poetry; Apollo; Clio, the Muse of History; and Calliope, the Muse of Epic Poetry. Inspiration for the composition came from several sources. Some of the figures had been reproduced by James Tassie in glass casts of ancient Roman jewels, and others were adapted from the engraving of the Sarcophagus of the Muses, now in the Louvre but once part of the Albani Collection in Rome.

330

Dressing Table

New York
Mahogany
Dick S. Ramsay Fund

About 1770
H. 33¼ in. (84.5 cm)
55.225

The selectivity of American taste is evident in the design of this dressing table; conservatism was apparently a matter of choice rather than the result of being out of touch with the latest fashion.

At first glance this appears to be a chest of drawers of traditional form, well made, and of fine mahogany. The square look of the claw and ball feet and the gadrooning along the skirt are decorative details favored by New Yorkers. Although distinctly local, these details were inspired by earlier English models. The top drawer, however, is another matter.

Divided into compartments with a book-rest, looking glass, and writing board built in, it resembles a suggestion in Thomas Chippendale's *The Gentleman and Cabinet Maker's Director*. In the third edition of that famous publication, plate 52 shows a French-style Rococo piece entitled "A Lady's Dressing Table," featuring this practical drawer. The New Yorker ordering this dressing table appears to have consulted the Chippendale book for the latest in gadgetry, but preferred to avoid the exuberant curves found in the prototype.

331

Desk and Book Case

Connecticut
Cherry lined with chestnut
Gift of Frederic B. Pratt

About 1770
H. 80 in. (203.2 cm)
15.477

The desk and bookcase, a furniture form now called a secretary, was known in the American colonies from about 1720 on. Large in scale, it was often elegantly carved. Here, however, is a simple version from Connecticut, the scene of remarkable rural craftsmanship. The cabinetmakers of this colony were practical in their approach to design and decoration. Classical motifs were abstracted into geometrical forms that were easier to handle, as in the case of the finials which were inspired by classical urn-finials on more elegant pieces.

In Connecticut, furniture evidences a dichotomy in the approach to design. Conservatism was one factor, as seen in the bookcase-doors with arcuated panels that would have been outmoded in Boston or Newport at the time. On the other hand, the blocking on the drawers of the lower section was definitely in fashion. The block-front desks and chests were among the finest products of both Boston and Newport in about 1770 when this desk-and-bookcase was made as a pleasing country reflection of the latest fashion.

Inkstand

Henry Will (New York, about 1736-1802)   L. 7⅞ in. (20 cm)
Pewter   45.10.142
Museum Collection Fund

The inkstand, or writing-box (to use the eighteenth-century term for it), is a container for pens, sand, and wafers used in letter writing. This example is an extreme rarity because so few pewter inkstands have survived. Pewter was of particular importance on the American scene in the eighteenth and early nineteenth centuries as a common material for household objects. Easy to form because it is relatively soft (but very perishable for the same reason), it served as an inexpensive substitute for both silver and pottery. American pewterers, like their compatriots in other crafts, preferred designs that were simple and functional.

Henry Will, whose mark is stamped on this box, was a member of a well-known family of pewterers active in New York in the eighteenth century. He worked in New York City from 1761 to 1775 and again from 1783 to 1796, maintaining a shop in Albany in the interim. His mark imitates the English hallmark, suggesting that the American product was held in less favor than the English import — much as American wines continue to be identified by geographic areas belonging only to France.

Tea Pot

William Will (Philadelphia, 1742-1798)   1764-1798
Pewter   6¼ in. (15.9 cm)
Museum Collection Fund   45.10.184

William Will, an outstanding American pewterer, worked in Philadelphia from about 1764 to his death in 1798. He was the brother of
Henry Will of New York and probably his apprentice. A broad range
of forms, superior workmanship, and handsome design characterize
his products.

This teapot is based on a shape known in English silver from the
second quarter of the eighteenth century and frequently expressed
in pewter until about 1820. Generally, pewterers were conservative,
using molds over a long period and disregarding changes in fashion.
The bands around the body of this pot relate it to examples by craftsmen active between 1760 and 1800. The perishability of this material
is proven by the scarcity of early work. In the newspaper advertisements of the 1750's, there are offers of "teapots of all sorts," but the
earliest surviving pieces date from at least a decade later.

336

337

Sugar Bowl

United States, attributed to
Henry William Stiegel (1729-1785)
Sapphire-blue glass
Dick S. Ramsay Fund

1765-1774
H. 6½ in. (16.5 cm)
40.9

This sugar bowl is an outstanding example of eighteenth-century American glass. The rich blue color and the faceted design achieved by blowing the glass into a diamond-patterned mold are characteristic of the factory operated by Henry William Stiegel in Manheim, Pennsylvania, from 1763 to 1774. Stiegel became an almost legendary figure in the lore of Manheim, evidently adopting the title of Baron and living in feudal splendor while his glasshouse was in operation. His account books and advertisements are proof of the wide range of products, larger than that of his American competitors; although this sugar bowl is logically attributed to Manheim, the eighteenth-century records are too general for specific identification.

Sweetmeat Dish

Bonnin and Morris
(Southwark, Philadelphia, 1769-1772)
Mark: P in underglaze blue
Porcelain
Museum Collection Fund

H. 5¼ in. (13.4 cm)
45.174

340

In the decade before the Revolution, the American colonists attempted to provide luxuries as well as necessities for themselves instead of relying on imports from home countries. American craftsmen had made furniture and silver in quantity from almost the first days of settlement. These, however, could be done in relatively small shops, while fine pottery required a more elaborate factory for production and, therefore, a larger investment and a more highly trained staff. Evidence of this kind of quality production is found in a newspaper advertisement which appeared in Philadelphia in December, 1769, announcing ". . . as good Porcelain, as any heretofore manufactured at the famous factory in Bow, near London . . ."

This bonbon dish is one of the group that has been attributed to Bonnin and Morris in Philadelphia. All are decorated in blue and white and reflect the style of wares produced at Bow and other English porcelain factories like Worcester and Lowestoft, although the body is thicker and the handling less delicate than the English examples. This thickness suggests a robustness that is particularly appealing and relates to the American approach to design seen in furniture and silver.

Can

Thomas Underhill
(New York, active about 1775-1790)
Mark: TU twice
Silver
Gift of Mr. and Mrs. Donald S. Morrison

About 1780
H. 4⅞ in. (12.4 cm)
61.201

American silversmiths tended to produce conservatively designed forms as simple variations of English work. The pyriform shape of this can or mug had been known for almost fifty years when Thomas Underhill chose to use it in about 1780. The curving lines and the ear-shaped handle with its leaf decoration reflect the Rococo style at the very moment when the more precise and linear Neoclassical style was being introduced on the American scene.

Thomas Underhill was a silversmith about whom little is known. He married in New York in 1779 and, when he became a Freeman in 1787, was listed as a partner of John Vernon whose Neoclassical silver is well-known. The quality of this can is evidence that Underhill was one of the many fine craftsmen active in New York at the time of the Revolution.

Figure of Africa

Frankenthal, Germany
Mark: lion rampant in underglaze blue
Porcelain
Bequest of James Hazen Hyde

About 1780
H. 9½ in. (24.1 cm)
60.12.29

The porcelain figure epitomizes the art of the eighteenth century in its intimate scale and delicacy. This fine material had been introduced to the West as a treasure from the Far East. The shapes and designs peculiar to the Orient were copied successfully long before the translucent ceramic body could be achieved; the secret of its manufacture — the use of kaolin and petuntse — was finally discovered by the German arcanist Böttger in the early eighteenth century.

This allegorical figure of Africa is part of a set of four representing the Continents. The elephant headdress and the lion were common attributes to be found in a number of engravings personifying the subject. The figure bears a mark on its base, the lion rampant, which was used in the porcelain factory at Frankenthal, near Mainz, in 1755 by Paul-Anton Hannong. Another copy of the figure, possibly from the same mold but painted differently and with a simpler base, bears the mark P H, standing for Paul Hannong.

Bed Rug

Connecticut River valley
Museum Collection Fund

1790
84 by 72 in. (213 by 183 cm)
48.189

This bed rug, or wool coverlet, is worked with a loose-running stitch in blue crewels on a home-spun, dyed and woven plaid blanket which is much worn and pieced. About seven strands of the yarn are used, looped high on the surface, resulting in a deep pile.

These bed rugs are said to have been made only in the Connecticut River valley, and always on a blanket ground. The soft, muted blues are typical of the region. The initials A. E. G. and the date 1790 are worked center top. The clam-shell motif was very popular and often used in quilting as well as embroidery. The coverlet provides an interesting example of the transformation of a worn covering into a new one by means of skillful needlework.

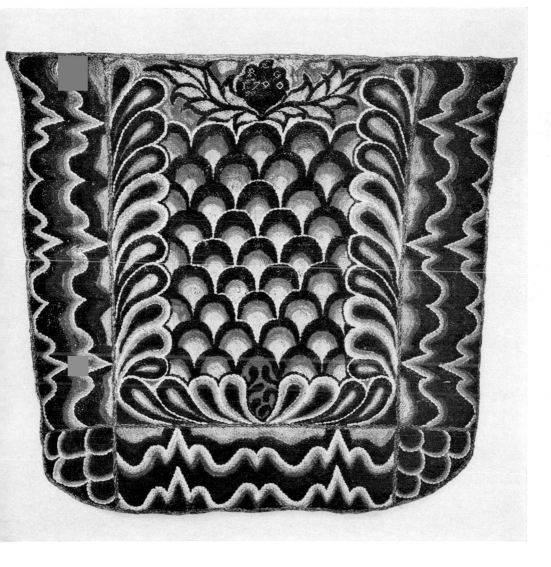

347

348

Chocolate Pot

China
Porcelain
Gift of the Wyckoff family

About 1800
H. 10¼ in. (26 cm)
41.1212

This Chinese chocolate pot is typical of the ware imported to the United States and called China Trade, Chinese Export, or Chinese Lowestoft porcelain. Close examination shows that the surface is mildly rough and slightly pitted, like an orange rind. The manufacturer mass-produced such pots, and they were not of very good quality; a completely different, extremely fine porcelain was produced in China for affluent noble households — the export wares suited American taste.

The shape of this vessel was dependent upon the needs of the Western market, but the decorative border, the handle, and the finial are in the Oriental tradition. Europeans and Americans were able to order specific subject matters or monograms. The initials under the spout, F. W., are for Folert Wyckoff (1778-1814), who is said to have received this chocolate pot as a gift from Captain Ebbits, a Brooklynite in the China trade.

Pie Plate

David Spinner (Pennsylvania, 1758-1811)   About 1800
Red earthenware with sgraffito decoration   D. 11½ in. (29.2 cm)
Gift of Mrs. Huldah Cail Lorimer in   56.5.8
Memory of George Burford Lorimer

One of the most delightful expressions of American folk art is the pottery produced in Pennsylvania in the eighteenth and early nineteenth centuries. Made of red earthenware covered with yellow, green, and brown glazes and decorated with sgraffito, or scratch, patterns, this pottery was produced in rural communities until it had to yield to the competition of inexpensive factory wares. The subject matters were generally copied from popular prints, and often a homely saying in the dialect spoken in the area was inscribed.

Here, the picture must be based on a contemporary racing print. The men on horseback are laying a wager: "Go for a half a Joe" which means "Let us race for half of a Johannes" (a Portuguese coin then common in Pennsylvania and worth about fifteen dollars). This plate is typical of the work of David Spinner who tended to be adventuresome rather than traditional in his subject matter. Born of Swiss parentage, he became one of the foremost potters of Bucks County. Most of his known decorative work dates from 1800 to the time of his death only eleven years later.

351

Tea Set

William Thomson
(New York, active 1809-1845)
Mark: W Thomson (twice)
Silver
Gift of Mrs. Chester Dale

About 1820
H. of tallest piece 8¾ in.
(22.2 cm)
64.76.1-4

In America, the Empire style was at its height at about 1820 when this tea set was made in New York. Based on the French modes of the Napoleonic era, the forms and ornament were generally Graeco-Roman in inspiration and heavy in scale. In this set, however, a variation in the choice of motifs is encountered as the decorative details derive from the realm of agriculture. Below the sheep finials is a band of bundles of wheat, and another band shows various aspects of farmlife. Substituting subjects of daily life for the mythological elements more often represented is one manifestation of the inventiveness of nineteenth-century designers.

353

Coverlet

United States
Wool and cotton
Gift of Miss Florence A. Boole

Early 19th century
L. 85 in. (222 cm)
W. 69½ in. (176 cm)
58.21

Cultivation of the textile crafts began early in the history of our country. Indeed, the need for cloth was so pressing at one time in Massachusetts that every household was required to contribute to its production. Even small children were taught to spin, and the rasp of the loom was familiar in many a household. Those who did not have their own looms would provide their own yarn — wool shorn from their own sheep, or flax, home grown, spun, and dyed — and then take it to a professional weaver to be made into cloth.

As the country pushed farther into the wilderness, itinerant weavers travelled from one hamlet to another, plying their trade. Sometimes the craftsman's name and date were woven in a corner of the quilt, — often the name of the person for whom the quilt was made.

The coverlet illustrated is of the type produced by the professional. However, this one, according to family tradition, was woven by a woman — the first woman permanently licensed to teach in Ohio. The coverlet is of the type known as summer-winter weave — that is, entirely reversible: a double weave was made with two warps and two wefts, light on one side and dark on the other.

Plate

Mark: oval with urn containing inscription:
"American Pottery Co./Canova/Jersey City"
White earthenware, "Canova" pattern
Museum Collection Fund

About 1840
D. 9⅛ in. (23.2 cm)
50.144

This plate is very much like the transfer-decorated creamware made in Staffordshire, England, during the nineteenth century. The mark it bears on the back is that of the American Pottery Company in Jersey City which did a very creditable job of duplicating the most popular imports from England. It was formed in 1833 by David Henderson and produced Rockingham wares and stoneware which also competed with Staffordshire products.

While the English potters attempted to suit American taste by using American scenes as the subject of the main design, it is amusing to see that the American Pottery Company chose to do an imaginary romantic view instead. The border pattern and the central design are simpler than those on better known English examples, a fact characteristic of most American ceramics.

357

Pitcher

Tucker and Hemphill
(Philadelphia, 1825-1838)
Mark: W incised on base
Porcelain
Gift of Mrs. Franklin Chace and
Dick S. Ramsay Fund

1832-1838
H. including handle 9¼ in.
(23.5 cm)
47.145

The porcelain of Tucker and Hemphill was manufactured in the French fashion with designs inspired by Empire models made at Sèvres. The scene on this pitcher has not been identified but many similar pieces have views of the Philadelphia area.

Tucker and Hemphill was founded by William Ellis Tucker in about 1825, and Judge Joseph Hemphill joined as a partner in behalf of his son, Alexander Wills Hemphill, in 1831; it closed in 1838. This output was advertised as including: ". . . a superior assortment of China, comprising Dinner Sets, Tea Sets, Vases, Mantel Ornaments, Pitchers, Fruit Baskets, &c." Although the firm did not employ identifying marks — save the one occasionally used by Joseph Hemphill after his son's death, "Manufactured by Jos Hemphill Philadelphia" — the molders usually scratched their initials in the paste. Our pitcher, marked with the initial "W," was molded by Andrew Craig Walker, to whom some of the best work of the factory is credited.

359

Parlor, The Robert J. Milligan House

Saratoga, New York

About 1853
24 by 16 feet (7.30 by 5.20 m)

This elegant interior of the middle of the nineteenth century was part of an upper-class dwelling based on a Renaissance-villa concept. Built in Saratoga, New York, by an affluent merchant, Robert J. Milligan, it is decorated in the Rococo revival style which represented the height of fashion in its day. As part of the early phase of Victorian design it was one of several styles used interchangeably. Technological changes affected the materials and the way of handling them, and differences in the patterns of living affected the size and types of objects in a parlor.

The suite of upholstered furniture with a matching center table is typical for the 1850's. It was made by Galusha Brothers of Troy and is closer to the French model than the more elaborate work of the New York cabinetmaker John Henry Belter.

362

Bed

John Henry Belter (New York, 1804-1863)   About 1860
Mark: J. H. Belter/Patent/Aug. 19, 1856/N.Y.   H. headboard 65½ in.
Rosewood   (166.4 cm)
Gift of Mrs. Ernest Vietor   39.30

John Henry Belter was the most famous American furniture manufacturer of the Victorian era, but most of what is attributed to him is
neither marked nor documented. He is credited with a good part of
the more ornate Rococo revival furniture made of laminated rosewood. This bed bears his name on one of its cross-boards and, in a
patent granted to Mr. Belter on August 19, 1856, there is a diagram
of a bed that resembles this one very closely. The patent is for the
construction, rather than the design, of the bed since it makes it
possible to set up and dismantle simply and without tools. Although
the technique of laminating, referred to as "pressed work" in the
patent, is described he makes no claim to its invention, stating: "I am
aware that veneers glued together with the grain of each layer standing at right angles to the next have been long in use for the purpose
of combining strength and lightness. This I do not claim nor do I
claim the above described method of producing it . . ."

Spice Container

Poland
Wrought silver
Gift of Mrs. Edward C. Blum

Mid-19th century
H. 7½ in. (19.1 cm)
49.228.8

Jewish ritual art includes all objects designed for use in the perform-
ance of domestic as well as ecclesiastical ritual, and although the
ceremonies are much older, the greatest wealth of collections of this
material dates from the eighteenth and nineteenth centuries. The
Museum collection of Jewish ritual art is meant to survey the objects
for each of the ceremonies performed during the year.

Spice containers, the most common of all Jewish ceremonial objects, served to hold spices at the Habdalah, the concluding service
after the Sabbath dinner. One would be passed around the table so
that the aroma could be enjoyed, the belief being that the fragrance
of the spice symbolized the hope for a full and happy week to come.

Flower and fruit forms for the spice container were developed
among the Eastern European Jewry. The Polish craftsman who made
this piece chose a shape that reflects the Neo-rococo style, which was
in vogue in the nineteenth century, in preference to the tower form
that had been used more extensively in France and Germany.

364

Dress

France, House of Worth 1880's
Gift of Mrs. W. E. S. Griswold 41.915

The House of Worth had been established over twenty-five years when this gown was made. It is of amber and brown striped silk moiré with pleated gilet of pale blue chiffon, and pale blue satin ribbon trimming.

Worth's early training in a draper's shop is reflected in his feeling for fabrics; the many hours spent in museums studying portraits may have been responsible for the sumptuousness of his styles.

Vase

Louis Comfort Tiffany (New York, 1848-1933)
Mark: scratched in script "L. C. T. X 1380"
Green glass
Gift of Mrs. Anthony Tamburro in memory
of her father, René de Quélin

About 1900
H. 10 in. (25.4 cm)
64.246.7

The American designer Louis Comfort Tiffany attracted the attention of the European art world when he introduced Favrile glass late in the nineteenth century. Using exotic forms and delicate, iridescent coloring, he produced decorative wares in almost unlimited variety. The attenuated shapes and his use of floral motifs make his work relate closely to Art Nouveau in Europe.

This vase is based on a Near Eastern form and has embedded striations in a feather pattern that is reminiscent of the decorative borders popular with book designers working in the Art Nouveau style. Besides his work in glass, Tiffany organized a decorating business that produced fine interiors for fashionable New Yorkers, working conservatively with reproductions of Chippendale as well as introducing more experimental idioms. The original owner of this vase was René de Quélin, head designer at the Tiffany Studios for ten years.

368

Prints and Drawings

Albrecht Dürer (1471-1528)

St. Eustace
Engraving
Gift of Mrs. Charles Pratt

1501
14⅛ by 10¼ in.
(358 by 260 mm)
57.188.22

Late mediaeval art in Germany culminated in the works of many gifted painters, engravers, and sculptors of the fifteenth and early sixteenth centuries. Albrecht Dürer of Nuremberg was the great exponent of this strong, creative current. His eminence as an engraver is reflected, for example, in the deep inspiration which his graphic work held not only for his own countrymen, but also for Italian and Flemish artists as well. His enormous skill of draughtsmanship and his brilliant use of the burin are evident in great measure in the engraving *St. Eustace*. Issued during the period between his two trips to Venice it is perhaps the most meticulously rendered of his larger engraved works.

The print illustrates the story of a Roman nobleman who, in the course of a day's hunting, encountered a stag bearing the Crucifix between its antlers. As a result of this miracle the hunter converted to Christianity and later became a martyr. Dürer represents the scene with a wealth of details in an elaborate but well organized composition. Its miniature-like refinement, precision of form, and richness of tone have seldom in the history of engraving been equalled.

373

Rembrandt Harmensz. van Rijn (1606-1669)

The Three Trees   1643
Etching and dry point   8⁵/₁₆ by 11 in.
Gift of Mr. and Mrs. William A. Putnam   (211 by 280 mm)
                                                    31.780.17

The Three Trees, one of fifty-three prints by Rembrandt in the Museum's collection, comes from a period in the artist's life when he explored the possibilities of dramatic and atmospheric effects in views of the Dutch countryside. Trees tower over the low lying plain, their shadows reaching to the small figures at the left. The great diagonal lines of the rays and the rolling turbulence of the clouds balance the dark zone on the right. This landscape unfolds into masses of sunshine and shadow with a grandeur and monumentality unequalled in seventeenth-century art.

Landscape has always been a favored subject of Dutch and Flemish painters. In describing the present print Jakob Rosenberg has stated: "*The Three Trees* of 1643, with its pronounced chiaroscuro, is full of Baroque romanticism which is quite exceptional in Rembrandt's etched work. Both in scale and in pictorial brilliance the artist here rivals his own paintings. The striking vision of the three trees, with massed foliage darkly silhouetted against a brightening sky, belongs among Rembrandt's most unforgettable creations."

Giovanni Battista Tiepolo (1696-1770)

The Magician Seated Observing Three Skulls 8⅞ by 7 in.
Etching (225 by 178 mm)
Frank L. Babbott Fund 34.141.18

Giovanni Battista Tiepolo's reputation as one of the great Italian artists of the eighteenth century is based on his numerous panel paintings and monumental fresco cycles. His graphic œuvre is less well known. The etching of *The Magician* is one of the most curious and provocative in his series of *Scherzi di Fantasia*. The monumental figure of the seated magician, the strange band of figures somewhat submerged behind him and the fragmentary relief of Roman soldiers in the right foreground, form a curious accompaniment to the three skulls and the other less obviously rendered symbols.

Alchemy, astrology, and black magic play a major role in many of the nearly fifty etchings that compose Tiepolo's graphic work. The concentration of the magician and the inscrutable symbols that make up Tiepolo's private vision are matched by the grace and fluidity of the artist's line and his ability to bathe the entire fantasy in a flood of dazzling light.

Trepolo

Jean Honoré Fragonard (1732-1806)

The First Lesson in Horsemanship About 1782
Pencil and sepia wash 13¾ by 17¾ in.
Gift of Mr. and Mrs. Alastair Bradley Martin (350 by 450 mm)
57.178

Fragonard, one of the great French masters of the eighteenth century, was idolized in his own time, and during the period in which this drawing falls he had become even more successful than his famous teacher, the versatile Boucher. During the 1780's Fragonard executed numerous family scenes and portraits. The Museum's drawing is typical of the studies made for paintings; its line is light and flowing and less formal than in his more meticulous paintings of the period. Here is a very personal statement by Fragonard depicting himself, his wife, his son, and the family dog. The mood is relaxed — a casual vignette of his family, reflecting, nevertheless, the elegance of Fragonard's style. An etching after this composition was made by Mlle. Marguerite Gérard, the artist's sister-in-law, and retouched by Fragonard himself. The Museum's drawing was formerly in the collection of Baron Edmond and Maurice de Rothschild.

Que pico de Oro!

Francisco Goya y Lucientes   (1746-1828)

What a Golden Beak!   1799
(From *Los Caprichos*)   7¾ by 5¾ in.
Aquatint and etching   (193 by 137 mm)
A. Augustus Healy, Frank L. Babbott, and   37.33.53
Carll H. De Silver Funds

Goya's splendid series, *Los Caprichos*, contains eighty etchings and aquatints of which this plate is number fifty-three. In the original announcement for *Los Caprichos*, published in the *Diario de Madrid* on February 6, 1799, appeared the following explanation: "Since the artist is convinced that the censure of human errors and vices (though they may seem to be the province of Eloquence and Poetry) may also be the object of Painting, he has chosen as subjects adequate for his work, from the multitude of follies and blunders common in every civil society, as well as from the vulgar prejudices and lies authorized by custom, ignorance or interest, those that he has thought most suitable matter for ridicule as well as for exercising the artificer's fancy." Goya's commentary on the above plate states in part: "Who knows if the parrot is speaking on some medical subject? But one shouldn't take his word. There is many a doctor who has a golden beak when he is talking, and becomes a Herod when prescribing . . ."

The preparatory drawing for this print is in the collection of the Prado Museum in Madrid. The Museum's collection contains eighty-seven prints by Goya including the complete series of *Los Caprichos* in the brilliant first and second states.

Honoré Daumier (1808-1879)

Enfoncé, Lafayette! . . . Attrapé Mon Vieux! 1834
Lithograph   11⅜ by 16½ in.
Carll H. De Silver Fund   (290 by 418 mm)
                                          39.542

The most distinguished and prolific caricaturist of the nineteenth century was Honoré Daumier. Although a brilliant painter as well, Daumier was forced to earn his living as a commercial illustrator on the Paris newspapers *La Caricature* and *Le Charivari*. This unusual lithograph, a masterpiece of political satire, shows the monarch, Louis Philippe, displaying public grief at the funeral of Lafayette, the leader of the opposition in the revolution of 1830. It is not surprising that both Daumier and his editor, Philipon, were imprisoned by the king for political criticism of the government.

Daumier's enormous versatility with the lithographic pencil is apparent in this print. The variety of blacks, the sensitive use of line, and the feeling for three-dimensional form give this composition a monumental quality seldom seen in the medium of lithography. This fine impression, one of sixty-four prints by Daumier in the Museum's collection, was formerly owned by Marcel Guérin in Paris.

382

383

384

James A. McNeill Whistler (1834-1903)

Drouet
Dry point
Gift of Mrs. Charles Pratt

1859
8⅞ by 5⅞ in.
(225 by 149 mm)
57.188.64

James Whistler, one of America's great artists of the nineteenth century, was maligned in his own time by conservative critics, but defended by the French avant-garde writers Marcel Proust and Charles Baudelaire. After learning to etch while employed by the United States Coastal Survey in Washington, he sailed for France to study art. In Paris, he made friends with the French artists, including Charles Drouet, the flamboyant sculptor and subject of this formidable portrait. One of ninety-five prints by Whistler owned by the Museum, the massive head of Drouet, delineated in this print by the rugged lines of the dry-point needle and the suave technique of the master draughtsman, gives this portrait a monumental quality. The sophisticated, sketchy treatment of the figure places emphasis on the magnificent head and suggests the work of an older master; Whistler was but twenty-five years old when he executed this remarkable work which he himself considered one of his finest prints.

Rodolphe Bresdin (1825-1885)

The Good Samaritan 1860
Lithograph 22⅛ by 17⅜ in.
Gift of Miss Clare de Saldern (562 by 442 mm)
33.58.19

Rodolphe Bresdin's lithograph, one of several owned by the Museum, was, by mid-nineteenth century standards, an unusually large-scale print; it was also the artist's most famous work. Born in the region of the Loire-Inférieure in 1822, Bresdin, often called Chien-Caillou, journeyed to Paris some twenty years later. After the Revolution of 1848 the artist left Paris for the south of France and subsequently took his family to Canada. The new environment, however, did not satisfy his wanderlust, and he returned to France through the friendly aid of Victor Hugo. Largely ignored and often denounced by the artistic world of his time, Bresdin's imaginative fantasies were nevertheless much admired by writers and poets, among them Charles Baudelaire and Victor Hugo.

In *The Good Samaritan,* the traditional figures in the biblical story are centered within an intricate and highly poetic landscape. It becomes an extravagant and gigantic fantasy wherein strange birds and vegetation merge into an engaging but wholly unrealistic world. Theodore de Banville described this composition as "the patient and furious work of a genius who desires to embrace everything."

387

Dante Gabriel Rossetti   (1828-1882)

Silence   1870
Crayon   41½ by 31¼ in.
Gift of Mr. Luke Vincent Lockwood   (1045 by 760 mm)
                                              46.188

Dante Gabriel Rossetti was the chief exponent of the Pre-Raphaelites, those who considered art before Raphael more important than anything produced thereafter. The artist is represented in the Museum's collection by this large and imposing crayon drawing which was first exhibited at the Royal Academy in London in 1883. The model is Mrs. William Morris, wife of the famous tastemaker, architect, and entrepreneur. In 1870, Mrs. Morris sat for Rossetti many times, and her melancholy features are identified with the strange type of beauty admired by the artist and his friends. With the exception of two pictures, Mrs. Morris appears in every work produced by Rossetti in 1870.

389

390

Edgar Degas

(1834-1917)

At the Louvre:
Mary Cassatt in the Etruscan Gallery
Dry point and aquatint
Museum Collection Fund

About 1879-1880
10⅝ by 9⅛ in.
(268 by 232 mm)
36.255.19

Until recently, few scholars have given proper recognition to Degas for his valuable contribution to printmaking. In 1879, along with Mary Cassatt and Felix Braquemond, he founded a magazine of original prints entitled *Le Jour et La Nuit*. This one, of Mary Cassatt at the Louvre, was carefully planned and printed in a number of states for publication in the magazine; this rare impression is from the fifth of six states.

Degas owned a press and printed many of the group's plates, as well as his own. After he mastered the craft he became a brilliant innovator using the various techniques in bold ways to achieve unique results. He was particularly interested in aquatint and its subtle tones which he felt would give the magazine a special distinction.

Winslow Homer   (1836-1910)

Eight Bells   1887
Etching   18¾ by 24½ in.
Carll H. De Silver Fund   (475 by 621 mm)
                                   35.1059

When Winslow Homer issued his second dated etching in 1887, print collectors were interested only in Whistler's prints and the French romantic etchers of the period. They considered Homer's work un-aesthetic by their standards, and the public whom the artist was attempting to reach found them too grim for their more sentimental tastes.

The present print — after a painting in the Addison Gallery of American Art — is characterized by Homer's forthright draughtsman-ship. It also reflects his fine ability to model the human figure in a strictly linear fashion, as he had done some fifteen years earlier in his wood engravings. The placement of the two figures on the right shows great originality of composition and a fine balance of tonal values.

The Museum owns five of the large etchings executed by Winslow Homer in the 1880's of which *Eight Bells* is the most famous.

394

Odilon Redon

(1840-1916)

Yeux Clos
Lithograph
Caroline Polhemus Fund

1890
12½ by 9½ in.
(312 by 242 mm)
36.490

Redon's lithographs span the last twenty years of the nineteenth and early years of the twentieth centuries. Among the French artists who inspired and influenced his work are Rodolphe Bresdin with his poignant images and new experiments in the technical aspects of printmaking, and Fantin-Latour whose graphic work was also an important departure from the usual lithography of the time.

The Museum's impression of *Yeux Clos* is one of the first edition of fifty and carries the artist's specific dedication: "à Jules Destrée cordial souvenir O. R." In this print Redon departed from his celebrated lithographic blacks and composed an eloquent work in pale greys. The inward intensity of the face is heightened by the closed eyes which seem to shut out the exterior world in order to more fully pursue a private vision. In his later portraits, including those of Maurice Denis and Edouard Vuillard, he returned to the soft subdued tones so brilliantly used in the *Yeux Clos*.

Mary Cassatt   (1845-1926)

La Toilette   1891-1892
Dry point and aquatint in color   10½ by 14⅜ in.
Museum Collection Fund   (268 by 364 mm)
                                                 39.107

In 1868, Mary Cassatt went to Europe to study painting; she settled permanently in Paris where she lived until her death. At the invitation of Degas, she exhibited her paintings and pastels with the Impressionists in Paris and became the only American artist to be prominently connected with the Impressionist movement. Although she began her long and fruitful experiments in the graphic arts in 1879, it was not until the following year that Mary Cassatt and Degas visited the large Japanese exhibition held at the Beaux Arts. What they saw there profoundly influenced the subsequent work of both artists. Soon thereafter, she produced her first prints.

Of the eighteen prints by Mary Cassatt in the Museum's collection, her most impressive graphic work is a series of ten in color completed between 1891 and 1892, of which *La Toilette* is number six in an edition of twenty-five. A combination of drypoint and aquatint, it was printed by the artist and M. Leroy and is so designated on the margin. Mary Cassatt's sensitive use of a difficult medium, her contribution to the technique of aquatint in color, and her painstaking press work are still studied and imitated by artists throughout the world.

Henri de Toulouse-Lautrec   (1864-1901)

Portrait of the
Comtesse Adèle Toulouse-Lautrec
Charcoal
Anonymous Gift to Commemorate
the 75th Birthday of Edward C. Blum,
February 24, 1938

1882
24¼ by 18⅛ in.
(614 by 460 mm)
38.39

During Toulouse-Lautrec's early years as an artist, he executed many remarkable drawings of members of his family and various family retainers at their country estate near Albi in the south of France. This portrait of his mother was done when the artist was eighteen years old and had begun his studies at the Bonnat Atelier in Paris. From 1882 to 1892, Toulouse-Lautrec concentrated on portraiture; the Museum's drawing falls at the beginning of this period. The seated figure is somewhat statically posed and "blocked in" in the best tradition of the classic art school. Stylistically, his debt to Degas and Forain is apparent in this drawing, while his primary concern, even at this early stage, was to catch the mood and character of his model. The Museum's collection contains twenty-nine prints by the artist.

399

400

Paul Cézanne

(1839-1906)

L'Amour de Puget
Pencil
Frank L. Babbott Fund

1888-1895
19¼ by 12¾ in.
(490 by 324 mm)
39.623

Between 1888 and 1895, Cézanne worked in Paris and Aix-en-Provence and was given, at the age of fifty-six, his first one-man exhibition by Ambroise Vollard, Paris dealer and publisher. Unrecognized, in fact scorned by critics and public alike, Cézanne was eventually acclaimed by three succeeding generations of artists: his Impressionist friends; the Symbolists; and finally as the father of Cubism.

This drawing is a splendid example of the many studies he made of works in museums. At that time, Cézanne preferred to carry pencil, watercolor box, and sketch pad rather than transport his painting equipment to the scene of his motif. Luminously rendered, *L'Amour de Puget* records his exceptional interest in Puget's sculpture in the Louvre, a cast of which he owned. In the Museum's version, Cézanne's pencil lingered on the rock behind the figure's left leg and transformed a dull area into a field of visually effective planes. He completed nine drawings of this particular subject.

Vincent van Gogh (1853-1890)

Cypresses
Reed pen and ink over slight pencil sketch
Frank L. Babbott and
A. Augustus Healy Funds

1889
24½ by 18½ in.
(623 by 468 mm)
38.123.19

One of the most distinguished drawings in the Museum's collection is van Gogh's *Cypresses*, completed on the grounds of the asylum in Saint-Remy in June of 1889. One in a group of drawings van Gogh sent to his brother Theo in Paris that year, it is obviously a study for his painting of the same title, now in the Metropolitan Museum. Made not long before his death, the artist's anguish is perceptible in the violent upward surge of twisted foliage. Far removed in style from his earlier dark drawings of Dutch peasants and landscapes, this work is spontaneous and uncluttered. The calligraphic quality of the swirling pen strokes reflects the artist's strong interest in the art of Japan.

Van Gogh discusses his deep interest in cypress trees in a letter to Theo (letter no. 596): "The cypresses are always occupying my thoughts. I would like to make something of them like the canvases of the sunflowers, because it astonishes me that they have not yet been done as I see them. It is as beautiful in line and proportion as an Egyptian obelisk."

404

Pierre Bonnard   (1867-1947)

La Blanchisseuse   1896
Lithograph in color   11⅜ by 7¾ in.
Museum Collection Fund   (288 by 196 mm)
                                     38.44

To color lithography Pierre Bonnard applied a painter's vision, with color playing an integral part of each composition. In the brilliant development of this medium his work ranks second only to that of Toulouse-Lautrec. The Museum owns thirty of Bonnard's prints.

Bonnard had already composed a number of lithographs for Ambroise Vollard before he executed *La Blanchisseuse* which was included in Vollard's *L'Album des Peintres-Graveurs* of 1896. Printed in red, grey, yellow-brown, and black in a limited edition of one hundred, it reflects the influence of the Japanese print and demonstrates Bonnard's ability to give commonplace themes both dignity and charm.

Regarded as a rebellious artist in his own time, collectors refused to acquire his work in color lithography because etching was considered the only proper graphic art. However, Bonnard's prints, lyrical, urbane, and occasionally nostalgic, have come to epitomize the close of a flourishing epoch in French art.

Edvard Munch (1863-1944)

Eva Mudocci 1903
Lithograph 23¾ by 18⅛ in.
Charles Stewart Smith Memorial Fund (604 by 460 mm)
38.253.19

Norway's outstanding painter, Edvard Munch, was also a distinguished printmaker. A moody and restless man, he travelled extensively at the close of the nineteenth century to escape his anxieties. During his travels, he studied graphic techniques in Berlin and at the Paris workshops of the master printers Clot and Lemercier.

This lithograph, also known as *Madonna* or *Lady with Brooch*, was executed in 1903 during Munch's successful sojourn in Germany where his work greatly influenced the artists of the Brücke. Although traces of Art Nouveau are apparent in this particular lithograph, it has a more powerful linear expression. The model is Eva Mudocci, a well-known Polish violinist, who posed for Munch also as a disturbing Salome and again as a performing artist.

Georges Rouault   (1871-1958)

Le Conducteur de Chevaux
Lithograph in color
Gift of Frank B. Hubachek

1910
13⅛ by 17½ in.
(334 by 445 mm)
39.554

Georges Rouault revolutionized fine printmaking in the early years of the twentieth century in his search for a medium through which he might express his religious convictions and state his own sense of impending tragedy. Rouault's first lithograph in color, *Le Conducteur de Chevaux*, one of two hundred and seven prints in the Museum's collection, is in the French tradition of Delacroix and Daumier. Its swirling movement and the glowing richness of the blues, yellows, and muted reds are combined in a vigorous composition. It is an auspicious forerunner of the many fine prints he created in the succeeding four decades, particularly for the publishers Ambroise Vollard and E. Frapier.

Rouault's graphics were akin to those of the German Expressionists. His lithographs reflect, as do his etchings, his complete disregard for the formal demands of the medium. Nevertheless, few have so fully exploited lithography and etching with such impressive results.

Lyonel Feininger (1871-1956)

The Disparagers 1911
Etching 8⅛ by 10½ in.
Dick S. Ramsay Fund (217 by 262 mm)
62.59.1

Feininger, one of the famous Bauhaus masters, was born into a family of professional musicians and, as a boy, studied music in the United States and Germany. In 1887, he decided to become an artist. After studying in art academies at Berlin and Paris, he supported himself by cartooning and illustrating for *The Chicago Sunday Tribune* until 1907 when he abandoned commercial art. By 1911, he was seriously absorbed in the modern movements of Cubism and Expressionism, and this year marked the turning point in his career as a fine artist. Although influenced by the French Cubists, he felt a stronger affinity to the German groups, particularly the Blaue Reiter and the Blaue Vier of which he was later to become a member.

In this etching, after a watercolor now owned by his widow, a romantic aura is present in opposition to the grotesque figures and the towering aquaduct in the background. Figures and architecture, although loosely rendered, seem to have a tremendous height, adding to the curious Gothic fantasy that is the artist's intention. The disparagers move through the landscape in a comic-sinister fashion and thus contribute to the charming eccentricity of this composition which is a strong transitional piece in Feininger's prolific œuvre.

410

The Disparagers

411

412

Georges Braque (1881-1963)

Fox 1911
Dry point and etching 21⁷/₁₆ by 14¹⁵/₁₆ in.
A. Augustus Healy Fund (547 by 379 mm)
  36.59.20

In 1911 Braque and Picasso were preoccupied with their joint venture
into Cubism. This large print, published in an edition of one hundred
by Henry Kahnweiler in Paris, was named after a Paris bistro fre-
quented by the poet Apollinaire and his artist friends during the
early years of the century.

It is possible that Braque's serious study of Cézanne led to the
analytical aspect of Cubism during this period. The carefully organized composition is an excellent example of the artist's use of planes
to show several views of a scene simultaneously; his restrained use of
the drypoint medium is in keeping with his analytical approach to
two-dimensional surfaces.

414

Pablo Picasso

(*1881)

Head of a Young Man
Conté crayon
Carll H. De Silver Fund

1923
24½ by 18⅝ in.
(621 by 474 mm)
39.18

Picasso's neo-classic drawing marks a transition period between his heavy-limbed nudes and his more elegant figure drawings and paintings of late 1923. Heavily stroked, its highlights are accentuated by the downcast eyes conveying a mood of serenity and introspection. This drawing, executed during the time of Picasso's great painting, *The Pipes of Pan*, has the same reflective concentration noted in the figure of Pan; also it is akin to the charcoal and oil painting of 1923, entitled *The Sigh*, in the collection of James Thrall Soby.

It has been observed that Picasso was a great draughtsman before he was a great painter. Whether he employs pencil, pen or brush, the artist easily suits his style to his medium, subject, or mood. In his classic studies of the figure he reduces natural forms to simple, solidly modeled contours and planes to make a convincing and harmonious whole. Although many diverse influences have contributed to this artist's vast œuvre, the present drawing reflects Picasso's interest in the sculptural forms of late Hellenistic art and the classical presentations of Diaghilev's Ballet Russe.

415

Pablo Picasso   (* 1881)

Minotauromachy   1935
Etching   19½ by 27¼ in.
Frank L. Babbott and   (495 by 692 mm)
Frederick Loeser Funds   59.30

Minotauromachy is the most important single print in Picasso's extensive œuvre. At the request of the publisher, Skira, Picasso composed several versions of the mythical minotaur who, according to legend, was half bull and half man. One of the versions appeared on the cover of Skira's avant-garde magazine *Minotaure*. During the years 1933 and 1934, Picasso made extended visits to Spain where he renewed his interest and indulged his fascination in bull fighting.

These two themes are woven together in this unforgettable print. Profoundly disturbed by the Spanish uprisings and growing tensions in Europe, Picasso cast aside his classical style and its flowing cadences. He turned to the symbol of the minotaur and the black shadow of the bull, majestic but terrifying in its primitive power. Picasso's anguish and his premonition of the impending destruction so soon to be unleashed in Spain were first given expression in this print. Rich in the personal symbolism of an exceedingly complex personality, *Minotauromachy* is a private allegory of considerable magnitude. Perhaps it also reflects the despair and hopes of the turbulent decades between two world wars.

The Museum's unusually brilliant impression of *Minotauromachy* carries a special dedication in the artist's own firm hand to the American artist Man Ray.

416

Jacques Villon (1875-1963)

Yvonne D. de Face
Dry point
C. A. L. Pratt Fund

1913
21⅝ by 16⅛ in.
(555 by 415 mm)
63.11

Jacques Villon, born Gaston Duchamp, was a member of an illustrious family of artists; he was the brother of Marcel Duchamp and Raymond Duchamp-Villon. The influence of a grandfather, an etcher, inspired the young Villon to serve an apprenticeship as a commercial engraver in Paris. However, he was soon involved in more creative activities.

Picasso and Braque were already working out Cubist theories and problems when Villon began his Cubist explorations of the portrait. At this early date Villon was developing his pyramid style, already apparent in this large portrait which is one of about a dozen prints that the artist made in the unfolding chronicle of Cubism. The Museum's impression, one of six prints in the collection, is number twenty-three of an edition of twenty-eight and was exhibited in the Salon d'Automne of Paris in 1913. It was originally in the collection of Dr. Oscar Stern, Stockholm.

418

Paul Klee   (1879-1940)

Portrait of a Pregnant Woman (Lily)   1907
Charcoal with watercolor wash   9⅝ by 13⅜ in.
Museum Collection Fund   (243 by 339 mm)
                                          38.110

This drawing, one of the important early works of Paul Klee, is a study for a composition painted in india ink on glass now in the collection of the Klee Foundation in Berne. A portrait of his wife Lily, it was executed in Munich shortly before the birth of the artist's son Felix. His wife was the pianist Lily Stumpf who shared Klee's knowledge and understanding of classical and romantic music. Although this sensitive study carries strong vestiges of Art Nouveau influences, it falls between the early period of Klee's satirical graphic studies and the beginning of that unexplored realm of fantasy which was to occupy the remaining years of his life. This portrait has the added distinction of being one of the earliest Klee drawings in an American collection.

421

Lovis Corinth   (1858-1925)

Death and the Artist II   1916
Dry point   7 by 4¾ in.
Gift of Benjamin Weiss   (178 by 123 mm)
                                            55.113.7

A great modern painter and a powerful forerunner of the German
Expressionists, Lovis Corinth was already an important artist when
he composed this revealing self-portrait. His preoccupation with death
was the result of a nearly fatal stroke in 1911, and this is one of many
compositions in which he portrayed death as a skeleton. The self-
portrait in this print shows a fierce man ravaged by illness and seemingly overpowered by the horror of his own mortality staring at him
from his mirror. Other than Max Beckmann, who in turn was influenced by Corinth, few modern artists have looked inward with
such piercing objectivity. *Death and the Artist* falls midway in
Corinth's great dry-point period when he became so adept with the
dry-point needle that he often worked directly on a copper plate
without a previous sketch. The Museum is fortunate to own seventy-
five of Corinth's finest prints, forty-six of which are dry points.

422

Lovis Corinth

424

Ernst Ludwig Kirchner (1880-1938)

Woman with Black Hat
Lithograph printed on yellow paper
Carll H. De Silver Fund

About 1908
23½ by 17 in.
(597 by 432 mm)
57.194.1

Ernst Ludwig Kirchner was one of the founding members of a group of German artists known as Die Brücke (The Bridge) which was organized in Dresden in 1905. Probably their most gifted member, he was their spokesman and driving force. Die Brücke occupies an important place in the development of German Expressionism as the first distinctly German movement in modern art. Their graphic work is often characterized by a deliberate coarsening of the medium to attain unstudied, stark, and strongly angular effects.

The present lithograph, printed in black on soft yellow paper, is one of Kirchner's most striking, early portraits. Heavy masses of black and a taut rhythm interspersed with softer lines produce an effect of inner tension and subdued emotion. The Museum has in its large German Expressionist collection eleven prints and a drawing by the leader of Die Brücke.

Max Beckmann (1884-1950)

Self-portrait with Bowler Hat   1921
Dry point   12¼ by 9⅝ in.
Gift of the Louis E. Stern Foundation, Inc.   (312 by 244 mm)
64.101.350

Max Beckmann, during his long life as an artist, worked on numerous self-portraits in various media; the present brilliant drypoint was issued in 1921. This was the time when Beckmann was actively engaged in revealing a new objectivity of vision, presenting the world of phantoms and dreams within a precise view of visible reality. Such an artistic approach mirrored, in the early twenties in Germany, a general postwar reaction to the pre-World War I movements of Expressionism and Futurism. The intense and searching expression of this full-face self-portrait reflects this point of view and perhaps served as an early sketch for Beckmann's formal painting of 1923, entitled *Self Portrait With a Cigarette,* now in The Museum of Modern Art.

426

Emil Nolde   (1867-1956)

South Sea Islander   1915
Lithograph in color   17 by 13¹/₁₆ in.
A. Augustus Healy Fund   (432 by 335 mm)
                                           53.254.3

Emil Nolde, the oldest of the German Expressionists, is known as one
of the truly great graphic artists of the twentieth century. His work
shows influences of the northern myths and of the, then newly discovered, primitive arts. The present lithograph, an artist's proof, is
one of a series resulting from his travels to Melanesia and Asia in
1913 and 1914. This fine head of a young native is composed full face
with great adeptness and economy of means in three colors: brown,
red, and black.

Emil Nolde grew up in north Schleswig, near the German-Danish
border. Christened Emil Hansen, he took the name of Nolde which
was the name of his native village. He was a lonely, often taciturn
figure, and his work reflects his preoccupation with the emotional
reality beyond a given subject or scene. Nolde came late to graphic
art as his first etching was made in 1904, and his work in lithography
dates from 1907. Nevertheless, he has to his credit a graphic œuvre of
some six hundred prints.

429

Arshile Gorky   (1904-1948)

Study for "They Will Take My Island"   1944
Crayon   22 by 30 in.
Dick S. Ramsay Fund   (560 by 762 mm)
                                             57.16

Gorky, a pioneer in abstract art in the United States, achieved, in the
last decade of his brief life, his most sensitive and eloquent drawings
and paintings. This is an exploratory drawing showing the artist's
linear journey into the unknown; the usual Gorky symbols are scattered and shifted throughout the composition. The claw, the foot, and
the amoebic forms interlock and overlap in the artist's search for a
solution to the problem of placement. All of Gorky's inventiveness is
displayed in this study — imaginary, floating forms, rubbed and
shattered lines probing the human anatomy. While improvising in
space, the artist invented a variety of new images. The painting that
directly followed this study is in the collection of Jeanne Reynal. The
Museum also owns one of Gorky's rare lithographs.

John Marin   (1870-1953)

Woolworth Building, New York, No. 3   1913
Etching   12⅞ by 10⁷/₁₆ in.
Dick S. Ramsay Fund   (327 by 265 mm)
                                             50.166.1

Although Marin's early work was influenced greatly by Whistler, the present etching and other similar ones, with their thrust and counterthrust of soaring lines, are Marin's personal response to the mood and tempo of New York in the first decades of the twentieth century.

Between 1904 and 1932, he issued about one hundred prints. In 1913, the year of the Armory Show in New York, the artist executed a number of etchings and watercolors of the Woolworth Building; the watercolors were already exhibited in the Armory Show while the etchings were done somewhat later. In a catalogue for his annual exhibition at the Stieglitz Gallery "291" Marin wrote: "Are the buildings themselves dead? We have been told somewhere that a work of art is a thing alive ... Therefore, if these buildings move me they too must have life. Thus the whole city is alive; the buildings, people, all are alive, and the more they move me the more I feel them to be alive."

432

John Marin

Woolworth — Main 13

433

434

Mauricio Lasansky

(*1914)

España

Intaglio

Dick S. Ramsay Fund

1956

32 by 23¾ in.

(813 by 603 mm)

59.12

Mauricio Lasansky had already distinguished himself as a graphic artist in his native Argentina before coming to the United States on a Guggenheim fellowship in 1943. After a productive year at Stanley William Hayter's Atelier 17, he accepted an invitation from the State University of Iowa to lecture on graphic arts where he remained to build and develop one of the best equipped print workshops in the United States. His great influence as a teacher on a generation of printmakers is well known, and his own creative work is prized by museums and collectors alike.

España, one of six prints by Lasansky in the Museum's collection, is a powerful protest statement in the tradition of Goya and Picasso. Just as Picasso expressed his horror of war in *Guernica*, so Lasansky, some twenty years later, criticized the Spanish dictatorship that allowed the murder of poets and children. The grief of the Spanish people is made dramatic through the use of deep blacks contrasted with the startling white of the melancholy rider. In this print, Lasansky pays homage to Goya's sharp social statements and his brilliant and audacious use of the etching medium.

435

Gabor Peterdi

(*1915)

Vertical Rocks
Etching
Dick S. Ramsay Fund

1959
33 by 23 in.
(837 by 584 mm)
60.65

Two imposing themes — landscape and the image of man — occupy the creative thought and energies of Gabor Peterdi. To both subjects he has brought a large measure of perceptiveness and an unusual knowledge of the great traditions of Western art. In his landscapes, whether in painting or in graphic work, the artist is concerned with the abstract elements that set the mood and control the movement of each composition.

The present print, one of a large group of intaglio prints and two large drawings in the Museum's collection, was issued after an extended journey through the Rocky Mountain region of the United States. It forms one of an important series in which the artist presents fantastic rock formations and their stark images as they appear against a seemingly limitless sky. Gabor Peterdi came to the United States from Paris in 1939 and since that time has contributed greatly to the eminence of American printmaking.

436

437

Leonard Baskin (*1922)

Angel of Death 1959
Woodcut 61½ by 30⅝ in.
Dick S. Ramsay Fund (562 by 777 mm)
60.60

A solitary figure in mid-twentieth century art, Leonard Baskin allies himself with the moralists and partisans of all ages. His large graphic œuvre, consisting of woodcuts, wood engravings, and etchings, is in the great tradition of Expressionism. This artist has issued prints ranging in size from that of a postage stamp to that of an ordinary door. They convey with passionate eloquence and often disturbing starkness a compelling note of social protest and a plea for the dignity of twentieth-century man.

In the present woodcut, the figure of death is crowded into the confines of a vertical composition with a cold finality heightened by the artist's own technical brilliance of rendition. The great size of the fiercely elongated figure serves to accent with dramatic insistence the artist's own concern with death as an avenging angel.

438

439

John Paul Jones   (* 1924)

Annunciation   1959
Etching   27⅞ by 24⅞ in.
Dick S. Ramsay Fund   (707 by 632 mm)
                               62.62.1

The American painter John Paul Jones was born and educated in Iowa where he studied printmaking with Mauricio Lasansky at the famed University of Iowa Graphic Workshop; later he taught the subject at the University of California in Los Angeles. *Annunciation*, one of his finest prints and one of five owned by the Museum, has won special acclaim for this young artist. The Museum's impression is number one of an edition of twenty. The subtle, dark nuances and the resulting mood of expectancy are achieved through the employment of a wide range of intaglio techniques. The dignity and aloofness of the central figure and the horizontal and perpendicular rhythms that hold the composition in balance, reaffirm Redon's idea of the relationship of the seen to the unseen — "putting the logic of the visible as far as possible at the service of the invisible." Unafraid of influences, Jones once stated, when it was suggested that his work bore a resemblance to that of Redon: "Why should I mind being like Redon? Redon is wonderful." Jones, through his imaginative vision and graphic talent, works in a similar realm of mystery and fantasy in the second half of the twentieth century.

440

441

Paintings and Sculpture

Maso di Banco

(active 1336-1369)

Tryptich
Tempera on panel
Gift of Mrs. Mary Babbott Ladd,
Mrs. Lydia Babbott Stokes, and
Dr. Frank L. Babbott, Jr.

About 1350
Center panel 21½ by 7⁷/₁₆ in.
(54.5 by 19 cm)
34.838

The art of the Middle Ages stood almost exclusively in the service of the church. In Florence in the early fourteenth century, the great painter Giotto developed a new style in his frescoes and panels that led away from the traditionally idealistic and flat compositional schemes. His figures, monumentally conceived, possess substance and weight and enact their roles with previously unknown dramatic intensity.

This small portable altar reflects Giotto's art in the work of his most gifted pupil, whose well-known frescoes decorate the walls of the Bardi Chapel at S. Croce in Florence. In the central panel the Virgin, represented holding the Christ Child, is surrounded by Saints; the two wings show Nativity and Crucifixion. Although the gold background invests the scenes with a mysterious light, the figures are built up as solid, three-dimensional forms and placed in a spatial context considered revolutionary for their time.

Carlo Crivelli (1430-1495)

St. James Major
Tempera on panel
Lent by Mrs. Frank K. Sanders
(Mrs. Ian MacDonald)

1472
37¾ by 11 in. (96 by 28 cm)
34.98 L

Venice was one of the great artistic centers in the history of Western art. In the late fifteenth century, the Bellini workshop included illustrious names such as Giorgione and Titian. Carlo Crivelli, who was born in Venice, left this city in the 1450's to work in various towns in the Marches. His style, still committed to Gothic tendencies, is more retrospective than that of some of his contemporaries. The figure of St. James is treated like a sculpture; the folds of the drapery are drawn in a hard, precise manner, face, hands, and hair are described in linear detail to give the figure a greater intensity of expression.

The altar-retable to which this panel once belonged was unfortunately taken apart before leaving Italy, and the parts sold separately. The central composition, with the Madonna and Child, has recently come to a private collection in New York while the other panels are preserved in the collections of the Metropolitan and Cleveland Museums.

St. James Major, brother of St. John Evangelist and cousin of Christ, is portrayed with his traditional attributes, the shell and the pilgrim's staff. His remains were brought to Spain in the seventh century where they are kept in the famous monastery of Santiago de Compostella.

447

Jan Cornelisz. Vermeyen (about 1500-1559)

Jean Carondelet
Oil on panel
Gift of Horace Havemeyer

About 1530
30¾ by 24½ in. (78 by 62.2 cm)
47.76

Jan Vermeyen, the son of a painter, was born in a village near Haarlem. A student of Jan Gossaert and a friend of Jan van Scorel, he was soon familiar not only with the rich heritage of Dutch and Flemish painting but absorbed also the Italianite influences conveyed through those "Romanists" who admired the work of the High Renaissance painters, particularly of Raphael. By 1529 he was employed in the service of Margaret of Austria, the sister of Emperor Maximilian, and in 1534 he entered the service of Charles V.

Cardinal Jan Carondelet, born in 1469, was a great statesman and carried the title of Chancelor of Flanders. The portrait illustrated here — probably the best of the artist's known portraits — is cast in the manner typical of the Renaissance in northern Europe. This is evident in the attention given to detail, in the clear drawing and sober color, as well as in the characterization of the sitter as an earnest and powerful man.

448

449

450

Aelbert Cuyp   (1620-1691)

Cuyp Designing after Nature   About 1650-1660
Oil on panel   11 by 17⅞ in. (28 by 45.3 cm)
Gift of Horace Havemeyer   56.191

In Holland, patronage of the arts was not limited to State, Church, and nobility, but rather was found in the rising and prosperous middle-class of merchants, businessmen, and even of prominent villagers. Dutch painting reflects the attitude of this large part of the population who desired to fill their homes with relatively small, intimate portrayals of people playing and drinking or in pursuit of their daily tasks, of views of familiar towns and the countryside, and of the abundance which graced their kitchens.

In this composition, probably the country around Dordrecht, where the artist was born and spent most of his life, Cuyp shows himself drawing the flat, horizontal expanse so characteristic of the Dutch terrain. The attention given to the costumes and gestures of the figures is matched only by the care devoted to the anatomy and stance of the horses. They are silhouetted against a luminous sky whose atmospheric softness is so typical of the new and naturalistic landscape tradition of the seventeenth century.

452

Giovanni Panini

(about 1691-1765)

Adoration of the Magi
Oil on canvas
Gift of Mrs. Thomas F. Walsh

1750-1760
39 by 29 in. (99 by 73.6 cm)
55.19

Giovanni Paolo Panini went to Rome as a youth and remained enthralled by the ruins of the Eternal City for the rest of his life. While archaeologists and architects busied themselves in making accurate, measured drawings of the remains of the ancient world, artists such as Panini were inspired by the gigantic remnants of a glorious past to create views of fantastic ruins around which were grouped religious, mythological, and genre scenes. In the *Adoration of the Magi*, as well as in its companion piece at the Museum, the *Adoration of the Shepherds*, the artist staged his drama through emphasis on architectural setting which, serving as royal shelter of monumental proportions, almost dwarfs the onrushing people and the subject of their awe.

Panini was born and trained in Piacenza where members of the famous Bibiena family, specializing in the building of theaters and in stage design, had worked. Through numerous commissions for frescoes, altarpieces and "trionfi," or decorations for triumphal receptions, he expounded the theme of the ruin in ever new variations.

454

Sir Henry Raeburn   (1756-1823)

Ann Fraser   About 1804
Oil on canvas   30¼ by 25 in. (76.8 by 63.5 cm)
Gift of Mrs. Arthur Lehman   53.141

British painting attained international importance with the art of the eighteenth century, represented by the work of Gainsborough, Reynolds and Hogarth, of Hoppner, Lawrence and Raeburn. Virtually all of the young American painters journeyed to London in the latter part of the century to study under Benjamin West and his illustrious British colleagues. The dominant theme was portraiture, which ranged from the comparatively simple, though psychologically deeply explored, likeness to the complex lifesize *portrait d'apparat* in the grand tradition of the seventeenth century.

A master of the former was Henry Raeburn, born into the family of a yarn boiler, knighted by King George IV, and appointed the King's Limner and Painter for Scotland before his death. At twenty-four, he married a widow of comfortable means and lived thereafter in Stockbridge, near Edinburgh, his native town, painting the wealthy of Scotland.

This work is executed in the painter's late style in which simplified composition, muted background, and a strong light all add toward a characterization of great immediacy and bold realism. The sitter was the daughter of William Fraser Esquire of Belnain (o. Inverness), a cadet of the House of Lords. In 1776 she married Alexander Fraser-Tytler of Woodhouselee, one of the Senators of the College of Justice and a Lord Commissioner of Justiciary in Scotland, an eminent lawyer and a prolific writer.

Jean-Baptiste-Camille Corot (1796-1875)

L'Albanaise 1872
Oil on canvas 29⅜ by 25⅝ in.
Gift of Mrs. Horace Havemeyer (74.5 by 67.5 cm)
42.196

The Museum's collection of French painting of the nineteenth century is particularly fine and includes many canvases of the Barbizon school and the Impressionists. Among the three Corots, this portrait is singled out as a remarkable example of the artist's late figurative style.

The reputation of Corot is based on his landscapes. His first visit to Italy, which he made in 1825, resulted in a series of luminous and clearly organized views of almost topographical accuracy. Later in his life when he painted in the forrests of Ville d'Avray and Fontainebleau he created those landscapes in which nature, quietly reposing in silvery mist and often peopled with ethereal maidens, achieved an almost Arcadian beauty. Like his friends of the Barbizon group, he explored the environs of Paris to find, in the stillness of the woods, the meadows and the tree-lined rivers, the motifs for his paintings that influenced so deeply his young Impressionist admirers.

In this painting, a fifteen-year old girl, Mlle. Darmelas, served as model. Introspective and romantic in mood, it resembles Corot's late landscapes. Alfred Robaut, whose catalogue raisonné of the artist's life work is of immeasurable importance, reported that this canvas had been reduced in size after leaving thc studio; originally the right hand of the model, holding some flowers, was visible.

457

Edgar Degas　　　　　　　　　(1834-1917)

Mlle. Fiocre in the Ballet of "La Source"　　1867-1868
Oil on canvas　　　　　　　　　　　　　　$51^3/_{16}$ by $57\frac{1}{8}$ in.
Gift of A. Augustus Healy, James H. Post,　　(130 by 145 cm)
and John T. Underwood　　　　　　　　　　21.111

Degas, by his association with the Impressionists and his participation in seven of their eight exhibitions held between 1874 and 1886, soon came to be considered a member of the group. Yet his methods were emphatically at odds with one of their basic tenets — "plein-air" painting. In criticizing a friend's work he said: "There's where you are wrong. You wanted to render the air out of doors, the air we breathe. But a painting, first of all, is the product of the artist's imagination." Unlike the Impressionists, Degas was more interested in the structure of the human body and in the subtle nuances in the movements of ballerinas, than he was in landscapes viewed through different atmospheric conditions.

On November 12, 1866, Paris witnessed the premiere of the Ballet "La Source," with score by Minkus and Leo Délibes and book by Arthur Saint-Léon. Eugénie Fiocre had the role of Nouredda — the central figure in our picture — in this woodland folk fantasy, set in the Orient. This canvas was accepted to the 1868 Salon and represents Degas' first attempt with the subject of the dance, which was to become the predominant theme in his oeuvre. Unlike those in his later ballet scenes, the performers are more like the actors in an historical painting, rather than dancers conveying movement in a fleeting moment of the dance.

458

Claude Monet (1840-1926)

The Doge's Palace 1908
Oil on canvas 32 by 39½ in. (81.2 by 100.3 cm)
Gift of A. Augustus Healy 20.634

On April 15, 1874, a group of young painters, already long dissatisfied with the system of jury selection at the Salon, exhibited their works on the second floor of a building at the Boulevard des Capucines in Paris. A few days later, a scathing review was sarcastically entitled: "Exhibition of the Impressionists." The term derived from one of Claude Monet's paintings exhibited, called *Impression, Sunrise.*

The Impressionists represent the most revolutionary movement in nineteenth-century painting. They worked exclusively out-of-doors to catch a moment of the day in constantly changing nature. Their aim was not a reconstruction of the world, based on academic studies carefully worked out in the studio, but rather they attempted to make visible the impression one gets when observing a brightly illuminated street or a field at mid-day in July. Without blending colors, they worked quickly with bold brushstrokes which fused optically in one shimmering representation of nature as it lay sundrenched and evanescent before the eyes of the spectator. To the Impressionists only sunlight makes all things come alive and sunlight dissolves forms that were so precisely modeled by the acedemicians in their ateliers.

Monet, the most typical representative of the group, found financial security only late in his long life. The paintings of the last decades before his death — like the series of Rouen Cathedral, the Venetian views, and the Waterlily group — become increasingly abstract as the artist's intentions to bathe water, trees, and architecture in intense light result in the melting of the objective world in brilliant, atmospheric vapor.

461

Paul Cézanne (1839-1905)

Village of Gardanne   1885-1886
Oil on canvas   36¼ by 29⅜ in.
Ella C. Woodward Fund and others   (92 by 74.5 cm)
                     23.105

Stylistically only loosely connected with the Impressionists, Paul Cézanne, in his paintings, gave nature a more structural character. His late work was to become a platform from which abstract art of the twentieth century took its course.

Cézanne came from Aix-en-Provence to Paris at the age of twenty-two to join his childhood friend Emile Zola. Although he frequently visited Paris in later years, he prefered to stay in the South, far away from the noise and heated discussions of the young artists in the City. This unfinished view of the village of Gardanne, near Aix, epitomizes Cézanne's art. Instead of dissolving forms in sunlight, as the Impressionists did, he saw nature in series of planes within a precisely organized, structural context. The houses of the village rise steeply toward the church at the center, painted in interlocked planes, the forerunners of Cubist art. Works such as this picture must be considered revolutionary at a time when sterile Academies strongly influenced the output of the more conventional artists as well as the taste of the public, and when only a small group of connoisseurs had just begun to appreciate the aims of the Impressionists.

464

Robert Feke

(about 1705-1750)

Unknown Woman
Oil on canvas
Dick S. Ramsay Fund

About 1748
$50^3/_{16}$ by $39^{15}/_{16}$ in.
(127.4 by 101.4 cm)
43.229

In eighteenth-century America there were no art schools, academies, or museums. Contact with the European painting tradition existed only through the occasional arrival of European-trained artists, the few paintings and prints brought to the colonies by settlers, and the circulation of inexpensive mezzotint portraits of famous personages. It is indeed remarkable, then, to view the accomplishments of a native of Oyster Bay, Long Island, Robert Feke, a largely self-taught artist. Although very little is known about his life, family tradition relates that he was carried off to Spain as a prisoner, but by 1742 he seems to have returned and married in New England. He worked between Newport, Boston, and Philadelphia from 1741 to 1750, painting, in the elegant tradition of the Kneller-Lely schools, wealthy colonists together with such incongruous backdrops to the American soil as baronial mansions and expansive landscapes. Portraiture, the dominant subject matter of this period, gives us a visual record of the Colonial family; Feke was the most accomplished among the early artists, endowing his sitters with a natural grace and providing them with the well-painted accoutrements of fashion.

William Williams (active 1746-1775)

Deborah Hall
Oil on canvas
Dick S. Ramsay Fund

1766
71¼ by 46½ in. (181 by 118 cm)
42.45

The name of William Williams has long been associated with the history of Colonial American painting, but it was not until this century that particular pictures have been ascribed to his hand. William Dunlap mentions him in his history in connection with Benjamin West [who] "... remembered him with gratitude as the man who showed him ... the first oil pictures he had ever seen." Williams, an Englishman, established himself in Philadelphia about 1746, where he painted portraits as well as theatrical scenery. In 1763 he advertised that, besides the business of "Painting in General," he also maintained an "Evening School for the Instruction of Polite Youth" where he taught drawing, painting, and music. About the time of the American Revolution, Williams apparently returned to England.

Deborah Hall (1751-1770) was the daughter of David Hall, a partner of Benjamin Franklin in the printing business. Of the known portraits by Williams, all make use of backgrounds which resemble stage sets rather than actual scenery and recall the artist's other profession as a scene painter. The charming classical conceit that surrounds Deborah is complete with urns, sculptured garden figures, and an allusion to classical myth, seen in the relief of Daphne in the foreground.

466

467

Charles Willson Peale   (1741-1827)

George Washington   1776
Oil on canvas   43¾ by 38³/₁₆ in.
Dick S. Ramsay Fund   (111 by 97 cm)
                                34.1178

Charles Willson Peale was an American "Universal Man." His many professions and enthusiasms included saddler, silversmith, writer, naturalist, painter, soldier, legislator, lecturer, dentist, and founder of America's first scientific museum. He approached art with the same headstrong passion with which he grasped his other crafts. Thus armed with Robert Dossie's two-volumed book *The Handmaid to the Arts*, the loan of a Copley painting to copy, and a few art lessons from John Hesselius for which he traded a fine leather saddle, he established himself as a painter. His progress encouraged friends to send him to London to study with Benjamin West (1767-1769), and upon his return, he ultimately settled in Philadelphia.

This portrait of Washington was the second of seven life sittings granted to Peale. Washington was called to Philadelphia for a congressional military conference in May, 1776. John Hancock, President of the Continental Congress, extended the hospitality of his home and, further, arranged to have the general and his lady painted by the young artist. To avoid political pressures, Washington stayed elsewhere but consented to having his likeness taken. The general is historically placed amidst his conquering force at Boston, while the city of Charlestown, Massachusetts, is seen blazing in the background.

468

John Singleton Copley   (1737-1815)

Mrs. William Eppes (Abigail Pickman)   About 1769
Oil on canvas   49 by 40 in.
Dick S. Ramsay Fund   (128 by 101.7 cm)
                                             65.60

The foremost American painter of the eighteenth century was largely self-taught. John Copley's early portraits are derived from mezzotint engravings after English prototypes and through observing the works of his older contemporaries such as John Greenwood and Joseph Blackburn. In 1755 he established himself as professional painter in his native Boston, and by the middle of the next decade he had attained the style that we associate with his best works. His portraits are invested with a clarity of observation, a strength and purity of drawing, and a luminosity of color that raise them to the equal of the best European painting of his time. Copley departed Boston on the eve of the American Revolution and traveled to Europe in order to improve his art by contact with the works of the Masters. He never returned to America but, in London, he associated himself with the Royal Academy, and the course of his career was altered.

Mrs. William Eppes is an example of Copley's mature style. The pose is sure and graceful, the composition monumental and yet intimate, and the painting of the head and drapery almost sculptural. Abigail Pickman (1733-1780) was the second daughter of Colonel Benjamin Pickman of Salem. She married William Eppes of Virginia in 1750 and was widowed in 1765. Three years after her portrait was made, she was remarried to Dr. Sylvester Gardiner, a Boston physician who established the first apothecary shop in that city.

470

471

Francis Guy   (1760-1820)

Winter Scene in Brooklyn
Oil on canvas
Gift of the Brooklyn Institute

About 1817-1820
58¾ by 75 in.
(149 by 190.5 cm)
97.13

By the beginning of the nineteenth century, portraiture ceased to monopolize American art. This charming scene, painted from the artist's window on Front Street, depicts his neighbors enacting their daily lives of feeding chickens, watering horses, sawing logs, or chatting with friends, in what was then the most important area of Brooklyn. Although Guy's interest was primarily topographical, his inclusion of the animated vignettes of everyday human activities created one of the earliest American genre scenes. This picture was damaged in a fire of 1890, necessitating the removal of approximately a fifth of the left side of the painting (see also p. 2).

Francis Guy left England, his birthplace, in 1795, after achieving a considerable reputation as "Late Dyer, Callendarer and Orris cleaner to the Queen and Princesses of England." His trail in the United States can be traced from Brooklyn to Philadelphia to Baltimore, where he resided for eighteen years; in 1817, he returned to Brooklyn for the last time.

473

474

Thomas Cole (1801-1848)

A View of the Two Lakes and Mountain House, 1844
Catskill Mountains, Morning 36¼ by 54 in.
Oil on canvas (92 by 137.2 cm)
Dick S. Ramsay Fund 52.16

The philosophy dominating America prior to the nineteenth century demanded a more practical approach to art than the enjoyment of nature. However, with the country secure as a prosperous, independent nation, the populace was susceptible to a surge of nationalistic pride in its scenic wonders. It was then that the landscape movement, known as the Hudson River School, began to gather momentum. Much of the excitement of the early canvases derive from the romantic glorification of native, virgin territory, untrampled by past civilizations.

Thomas Cole, the principal leader of this national school, was English-born. Trained as an engraver, he came to America with his family in 1818 and made several moves before settling in New York in 1825. Perhaps inspired by the sale of three early canvases to Trumbull, Durand, and Dunlap, all artists of repute, he launched a successful career as a landscape painter.

Cole is chiefly remembered for the vast panoramas of the Catskill territory, filled with meticulously drawn details, such as the jagged boulders or the gnarled tree that became the romantic signature of the Hudson River landscapists. The house seen in the upper left of the composition is a famed hotel, built in 1823 and later called the Beach Mountain House for its owner, Charles L. Beach.

George Caleb Bingham   (1811-1879)

Shooting for the Beef　　　　　　1850
Oil on canvas　　　　　　　　　　33½ by 49¼ in. (85 by 125 cm)
Dick S. Ramsay Fund　　　　　　40.342

Bingham lived during the period of westward expansion, and his art reflects the spirit of pioneer life. Taken as a child by his parents from an established home in Virginia to frontier Missouri, he grew up in an environment of roistering boatmen and backwoods political and social activities. By 1835 he was already known in Columbia, Missouri, for his solid likenesses of local worthies — portraits that earned him twenty dollars and critical notice in the local newspaper. Bingham returned to the East in 1837 where he sought further instruction at the Pennsylvania Academy; he later lived in Washington, D. C. After several years of study during the late 1850's in Düsseldorf, he returned to Missouri, there to spend the balance of his years.

Although he earned a livelihood painting portraits, Bingham is best known for his genre subjects. These he drew with solidity and assurance, charging them with rich color. His scenes of country life, often bathed in a warm afternoon light, seem to be poignant reminders of a vanished America. Nearing the end of his life, Bingham remarked that his efforts were intended to "... assure us that our social and political characteristics ... will not be lost in the lapse of time for want of an Art record rendering them full justice." *Shooting for the Beef* celebrates a typical event in the life of the pioneer community as a gathering of marksmen assembles in competition.

476

477

Eastman Johnson (1824-1906)

Not at Home
Oil on canvas
Gift of Gwendolyn O. L. Conkling

About 1860-1865
26½ by 22¼ in.
(67.3 by 56.5 cm)
40.60

Eastman Johnson was born in rural Maine and received his first art training in a lithographer's studio in Boston. Returning to his home state in the early 1840's, Johnson set himself up in his family's house and advertised his availability to do portraits in crayon. After sojourns in Washington and Boston, he went to Düsseldorf to study at the Academy; however, he soon departed the laborious routine of the school in favor of studying directly from the Dutch masters in the museum at The Hague. The subdued light and subtle color of the Dutch seventeenth-century masters proved to be a formative influence. Johnson returned to the United States in 1855 and painted a series of genre scenes of the Old South that culminated with a number of important Civil War subjects. Country life around Nantucket began to attract Johnson's interest in the 1870's at the same time that he was painting ambitious "conversation pieces" of prosperous New York families.

It is from this period that *Not at Home* originates. Its effect is borrowed from a Dutch little-master's interior. In spite of the profusion of detail, the painting is unified by the play of shadow and reflected light and is given a psychological intensity by the fleeting presence of the figure on the darkened stair.

Frederic Edwin Church (1826-1900)

South American Landscape
Oil on canvas
Dick S. Ramsay Fund

1873
38⅜ by 59⅞ in. (100 by 152 cm)
63.150

Frederic Church, born in Hartford of a prosperous family, shunned the education of a gentleman and turned to painting as a career. He studied with Thomas Cole, living at Cole's house at Catskill on the Hudson where he applied himself at mastering the art of landscape painting. By the time he was twenty, he was being acclaimed for an extraordinary accuracy of vision in which he fused intricate detail with enveloping light in views of the Hudson River and the Catskill mountains.

Church sought to explore the diversity of nature and to render it with clarity and an almost scientific objectivity. Unlike most of his contemporaries who flocked to Europe in search of instruction from established academies or the nostalgic remains of the past, Church turned his eyes toward the vast wilderness of the Western Hemisphere. Upon reading the journals of Alexander von Humboldt he became fired with the desire to paint the wonders of the South American continent. He went on two trips to Ecuador and Columbia in 1853 and again in 1857. His *Heart of the Andes* of 1859, now at the Metropolitan Museum, made him the most famous American artist of his time. The *South American Landscape* was painted as a commission from Robert Hoe of New York, a well-known art patron. Composed in the studio from sketches made during Church's travels, the scene probably represents the valley of Santa Isabel in Columbia.

George Inness   (1825-1894)

June   1882
Oil on canvas   30¼ by 45 in.
Bequest of Mrs. William Putnam   (76.8 by 114.3 cm)
                                   41.776

In stark contrast to the sharply focused vistas of wilderness depicted by the Hudson River School, George Inness preferred the friendly Jersey countryside he knew so intimately. Having been trained as a map engraver and having studied under Régis Gignoux, his early work is executed in a tight style. However, after successive visits to Europe between 1847 and 1875, he became deeply interested in the Barbizon landscape school. His paintings, veiled in a vaporous mist of color and light, reflect the pastoral mood so evident in the works of the French examples. His naturalistic concern with the time of year is here evidenced by spring-green foliage in full blossom, not yet exhausted nor charred by the hot summer sun. In his later paintings, for which he is best known, meadows and trees are enveloped in a dark and burning atmosphere, and forms evolve into mystical shadows.

Thomas Eakins (1844-1916)

Oarsmen on the Schuylkill
Oil on canvas
The Woodward Memorial Funds

About 1873
27 by 47½ in.
(68.5 by 120.5 cm)
30.14

In the paintings of Thomas Eakins, American art reached its apogee in the nineteenth century. No other single painter so surely combined the poetic vision and keenly intellectual mind that Eakins brought to bear upon the problems of realism in painting. While a student in the art classes of the Pennsylvania Academy in his native Philadelphia, Eakins also found time to apply himself to the problems of human anatomy as taught in nearby Jefferson Medical College. Equipped with such solid grounding, he went to Paris in 1866 and sought further instruction from Gérôme and Léon Bonnat. But the most powerful formative influence came to Eakins through the study of those masters of Spanish realism, Velazquez and Ribera. Although Impressionism was beginning to make an impact in Europe at this time, Eakins preferred to address himself to the world of solid form and broadly-handled light.

Eakins' art took for its subject matter themes of a robust nature. Fond of sport, he was drawn to scenes of athletic activity. One of the most characteristic series in Eakins' œuvre is that of *Oarsmen on the Schuylkill,* painted shortly after his return to the United States. The luminous afternoon atmosphere and the finely felt relationship of the solid forms of oarsmen against the transparent air and water are constructed upon a thoroughly understood observation of nature.

486

Thomas Eakins (1844-1916)

Letitia Wilson Jordan Bacon 1888
Oil on canvas 59 by 40⅛ in. (151 by 102 cm)
Dick S. Ramsay Fund 27.50.19

Eakins returned to Philadelphia in 1870, to spend the rest of his life working against the indifference and hostility that met him at every turn. He did not believe that an artist should escape to a friendly environment in order to perfect his work; rather, he seemed to regard difficulties as a stimulus. With the completion of *The Gross Clinic* in 1875, Eakins achieved a painting so powerful in its descriptive realism that it was labeled as a "degradation of art." The following year, he joined the faculty of the Pennsylvania Academy, where he reorganized the teaching by using nude models in the life class. The prudery of the times saw harm in this, and Eakins was eventually driven to resign his position.

Mrs. Letitia Wilson Jordan Bacon was the sister of David W. Jordan, a landscape painter, pupil and friend of Eakins. The wistful expression that Eakins achieves in Letitia Bacon's likeness is characteristic of his treatment of female sitters. Here, the feeling is heightened by the costume, a party dress whose ornateness stands in dramatic contrast with the surrounding emptiness.

Thomas Eakins   (1844-1916)

William Rush Carving his Allegorical Figure   1908
of the Schuylkill River   36 by 47¾ in.
Oil on canvas   (91.5 by 120.6 cm)
Dick S. Ramsay Fund   39.461

Eakins regarded the study of the nude as the most severe test of discipline for the artist. Unlike so many of his contemporaries, who saw it as a vehicle for a warmedover Classicism, he painted the nude only when the occasion justified it. As a realist, he did not believe that this subject could be made meaningful in painting without a logical relationship between it and the actual world. He said, "... I can conceive of few circumstances wherein I would have to paint a woman naked, but if I did I would not mutilate her for double the money. She is the most beautiful thing there is — except a naked man." Those circumstances were limited to the painting of a Crucifixion, a group of male swimmers, and a series of female nudes that expound on the theme of the sculptor William Rush and his model.

The inital statement of the Rush theme occurred in 1877. William Rush (1756-1833) represented a kind of ideal to Eakins, who identified with the early sculptor's efforts to use a nude model for his carving of the allegorical figure which Eakins regarded elegant and beautiful. The second completed version of this painting came in 1908, accompanied by two variations on the theme and a number of wax models that Eakins used for anatomical study. In the Brooklyn painting, Eakins has attempted to recreate the atmosphere of Rush's studio; the figure of Rush and the chaperone recede into the background and accentuate the sculptural volume of the nude.

488

490

Winslow Homer (1836-1910)

In the Mountains
Oil on canvas
George C. Brackett Fund

1877
24 by 38 in. (61 by 96.5 cm)
32.1648

Consistent with the beginnings of many careers in the history of nineteenth-century American art, Homer was trained as an apprentice in a lithographic workshop. For seventeen years, he was primarily occupied as a free-lance illustrator for *Harper's Weekly*. During the Civil War he produced his first oil painting, and to this work he transferred a powerful, objective realism. In 1866, he spent a few months in Paris; however, believing that "an artist must never look at pictures," he returned to the United States only the more certain of his own vision. While continuing to work as magazine illustrator, Homer translated scenes of human activity into a painterly genre that is notable for its absence of sentimentality. With subjects as diverse as New England farm life, children's games, Adirondack hunters, and the social activities of New Jersey summer resorts, he created paintings imbued with luminous color and well-defined patterns of light and dark. Rather than using color and light to dissolve form in the manner of the Impressionists, Homer strived to achieve clarity and definition.

Of all trends present in the Paris of 1867, Homer seems to have assimilated only one: Japanese design. This was noted by his contemporaries as early as 1879. *In the Mountains* displays a feeling for bold composition in the strong diagonals and muted color pattern which almost imperceptibly reflect this influence.

492

Winslow Homer   (1836-1910)

The Turtle Pound   1898
Watercolor on paper   16 by 21⅜ in.
Alfred T. White Memorial Fund and others   (40.6 by 54.3 cm)
                                               23.98

Upon his return to the United States in 1883, Homer established his home and studio on the coast of Maine, in the small fishing community at Prout's Neck. During the 1880's, he concentrated on the theme of the heroic encounter of men with the sea. Later, he gradually withdrew the human element from the subject matter of his oil paintings and concentrated upon the timeless struggle between the relentless sea and the obdurate granite coast. Throughout the latter period of his life, Homer made extended yearly trips to the Adirondacks and the Canadian woods, to the lush verdure of Florida and to the brilliant waters of the Caribbean. A convenient method by which to make notations during his travels watercolor became, in Homer's hands, the means for finished expression.

While Homer chose to paint the elemental, lonely face of the Maine coast, he frequently returned the human reference to the watercolors of his final years. Tropical scenes such as *The Turtle Pound* are filled with light, and yet there is the underlying theme of danger which was the violent aspect of the tropics, symbolized in other pictures by the shark and the hurricane.

494

John Singer Sargent   (1856-1925)

Paul Helleu Sketching, and his Wife   1889
Oil on canvas   25⅝ by 31¾ in.
Museum Collection Fund   (65.1 by 80.6 cm)
                                              20.640

Sargent entered the Paris studio of the portrait painter Carolus-Duran, and during the years 1874-84 rose from the position of talented student to become a rival of his former teacher. In 1884, Sargent submitted *Portrait de Mme X* to the Salon exhibition and found himself immediately plunged into what his friend Henry James called "an unreasoned scandal." (The painting is now in the Metropolitan Museum.) The consequences were disastrous for his career in Paris. No client wished to risk being exposed to such objective and searching portraiture. In 1885, Sargent moved his studio to London where he began his career anew. From this time until 1889, his summers were spent in rural Worcestershire where he experimented with a modified Impressionism. Sargent had fallen under the influence of Claude Monet perhaps as early as 1876, and a close friendship existed between the two. In England, Sargent began to paint a large group of landscape subjects in which the element of light is pre-eminent. His most celebrated canvas from this period, *Carnation, Lily, Lily, Rose*, captures the elusive quality of twilight and was painted entirely *plein air*.

Of all of his pictures from the Worcestershire period, the informal portrait of the Helleus comes closest to the ideal of pictorial harmony and balance between subject matter and technique. Paul Helleu (1859-1927) was a friend from student days in Paris and, when this painting was made, was on his wedding trip. Sargent shows him painting by the River Avon, the scene bathed in a warm, indirect light.

John Frederick Peto (1854-1907)

Still Life with Lanterns
Oil on canvas
Dick S. Ramsay Fund

After 1889
50 by 30 in. (127 by 76.2 cm)
48.166

Still-life painting, which had finally emerged in American art with the intimate works of James and Raphael Peale, found later practitioners in John F. Francis and Severin Roesen. Philadelphia became a center for the development of a "school" of still-life painting that has been attributed to a particularly American love of fact. The development of the camera, too, must be credited for the rise of an intensive *trompe-l'oeil* tradition that, in the hands of lesser members of the school, became mere deception.

John Peto, like his more famous contemporary, William Harnett, was born in Philadelphia. His style of painting is so close to that of Harnett that Peto's identity became lost in time. A retiring person, Peto kept to himself for much of his life. Between 1889 and his death, he lived in virtual isolation in a small summer resort on the coast of New Jersey, and only in recent years has he emerged as an artist in his own right. Unlike Harnett, who lavished attention on textures and whose surfaces are lustrous and compositions forceful, Peto tended toward a soft, atmospheric tonality in his pictures. His compositions are less rigid, and his subject matter is often sentimental.

497

John Sloan   (1871-1951)

Haymarket   1907
Oil on canvas   26 by 31⅞ in. (66 by 81 cm)
Gift of Mrs. Harry Payne Whitney   23.60

At the turn of the century, the American art academies had grown powerful but staid in their eclectic tastes, their complete reliance on standards of technical proficiency, and their restriction of membership and exhibition privileges. In rebellion, a group of artists, known as "The Eight" and by later critics as the "Ash Can School," joined together under the leadership of Robert Henri and exhibited their work at Macbeth's Gallery in New York in February, 1908; this exhibition shook the complacent American art scene. Although there was a diversity of styles represented within the group, the majority of canvases were of dark tonality, — a reaction to the bright vagaries of the increasing number of American Impressionists — depicting with much gusto the city life about them. Like Sloan, four of the Eight had begun their careers as reporters on Philadelphia newspapers, an experience that led them to paint the lower strata of society in an abbreviated, realistic, and often humorous style.

Of this canvas Sloan later commented: "This old dance hall on Sixth Avenue (and 14th Street), famous through infamy, was a well-known hangout for the underworld. Ladies whose dress and general deportment were satisfactory to the doorman were admitted free. Gents paid."

William Glackens (1870-1938)

Nude with Apple 1910
Oil on canvas 40 by 57 in. (101.5 by 144.8 cm)
Dick S. Ramsay Fund 56.70

William Glackens was thirty-eight when he joined the revolt of the group of younger American artists known as "The Eight." Glackens had studied at the Pennsylvania Academy and, for a time, worked also as a pictorial journalist for a Philadelphia newspaper before going to Paris. He returned to New York where he worked again as an illustrator for newspapers and magazines. Together with George Luks, John Sloan, and Everett Shinn, Glackens believed in "the importance of *Life* as the primary motive of art." Their source of inspiration was found in the everyday verities of contemporary life, and far from producing scenes of coarseness and ugliness, as they were often accused of doing, The Eight rejoiced in the color and vitality they found about them.

At the turn of the century, Glackens painted portraits that show his admiration for Henri. But the dark tonalities, present even in his landscapes, soon gave way to a brighter palette as he came under the sway of French painting, notably that of Renoir. His *Nude with Apple* reveals the essential qualities of Glackens's temperament: he was a witty, but cool and somewhat detached, observer.

501

Jack Levine   (*1915)

Welcome Home	1946
Oil on canvas	40 by 60 in.
The Woodward Memorial Funds	(101.4 by 152.2 cm)
	46.124

Today, the realism of The Eight seems mild, indeed nostalgic. These artists were followed by men who looked at the contemporary scene and were displeased with what they saw. They commented accusingly and with biting sarcasm.

Jack Levine wrote of this picture: "In painting *Welcome Home* my desire was above all to express the feelings of the enlisted men who served in the wartime army and had to submit to a caste system which violated every instinct that had been nurtured within them. A civilian could not have conceived of *Welcome Home*, and only an audience of ex-G. I.'s can fully appreciate its comedy. It is a comedy. However this is not apparent to generals, who have seen the painting. They act as though their noses have been tweaked ... Years ago I made a drawing of an old man chewing. I decided: I will paint a general at a banquet and no matter how commanding and impressive a general — he will be chewing. His wife however smart and fashionably turned out — will be chewing. Everybody in the general's party will be chewing as a gesture of kinship with the lower orders of mankind. What is more absurd than an august gathering, abstractedly chewing their cuds, vacantly eyeing the table, each other and infinity, awaiting the release that comes when the mouthful is ground fine enough to be swallowed?"

Charles Sheeler (1883-1965)

Incantation   1946
Oil on canvas   24 by 20 in. (61 by 50.8 cm)
The Woodward Memorial Funds   49.67

The title *Incantation*, with its implication of magical powers, expresses the awe Sheeler felt toward modern life and its machines. A tenuous balance between the extremes of abstraction and realism is maintained in this canvas by the telescoping of precisely drawn industrial forms, somehow disjointed from a larger recognizable scene.

Sheeler came to this style through an early familiarity with the work of the French Cubists and his own development in the field of photography from which he earned his livelihood for many years. In the work of this artist the absence of human forms and the inhabitability of his scenes coincide with his stated objective: to give his canvases "the absolute beauty we are accustomed to associate with objects suspended in a vacuum."

Larry Rivers   (*1923)

July   1955
Oil on canvas   83⅛ by 89¾ in. (216.3 by 228 cm)
Anonymous gift   56.160

Larry Rivers grew up in the Bronx, and not until about 1947, when he began to study painting with Hans Hofmann, had he made a serious effort at a career in art. In the mid-1940's, the leaders of the New York school of abstract painting were Pollock, de Kooning, and Gorky. Rather than follow the lead of this powerful influence, Rivers set his art upon paths which have been termed "reactionary" in that he has always been concerned with a reference to surface realism and the illusion of light in his canvases.

Often the representations of faces or figures in his paintings take on the quality of measured time, as the spectator becomes aware of shiftings, of double, and sometimes triple, images of the same subject. Rivers sees no need to treat landscape subjects differently than portraits; there is the same prevailing ambiguity of time and place, the same suggestion of evanescent light and form. His painting employs a tentative, muted, but rich coloration applied in thin, sketchy washes. Especially in a painting like *July*, Rivers evokes a mood of nostalgia by the deliberate frontality of the figures, as in an old snapshot.

Hiram Powers   (1805-1873)

The Greek Slave   1869
Marble   H. 66 in. (167.6 cm)
Gift of Charles F. Bound   55.14

From an early folk tradition of carvers of ship mastheads, welders of weathervanes, and engravers of tombstones, there emerged an American school of sculpture. Arriving late on the artistic scene it sought to rival the art of ancient Greece.

Encouraged by the success of other sculptors such as Antonio Canova, access to the arts of the ancient and Renaissance worlds, and the inexpensive costs of labor, Powers removed to Florence in 1837. The pinnacle of his career was the creation of *The Greek Slave* which, when exhibited at the Crystal Palace in London for the 1851 Universal Exhibition, brought the artist and his work immediate acclaim; reviewers and poets were ecstatic, other exhibitions were organized around this piece, and there was much clamor for duplications. The work exists in six full-size versions of which the earliest dates from 1843.

The posture of *The Greek Slave* derives from the Venus of Knidos. The theme has been described by the artist himself: "... I remembered reading of an account of the atrocities committed by the Turks on the Greeks during the Greek revolution .... During the struggle the Turks took many prisoners, male and female, and among the latter were beautiful girls, who were sold in the slave markets of Turkey and Egypt. These were Christian women, and it is not difficult to imagine the distress and even despair of the sufferers while exposed to be sold to the highest bidders. But as there should be a moral in every work of art, I have given to the expression of the Greek Slave what trust there could still be in a Divine Providence for a future state of existence, with utter despair for the present, mingled with somewhat of scorn for all around her."

Gaston Lachaise (1882-1935)

Standing Woman 1932
Bronze H. 88½ in. (223 cm)
Alfred T. White Memorial Fund and others 56.69

Of the foreign-born artists, who came to the United States, Gaston Lachaise was one of the greatest talents in contemporary sculpture. Encouraged to come to this country by his friend and patroness, Mrs. Isabel Nagel, Lachaise arrived in Boston in 1906 and worked for the following six years as a sculptor's assistant. By 1912, he had moved to New York, assisting Paul Manship with important commissions in the city. This year saw the beginnings of the most important recurring theme of Lachaise's career, that of the buoyant, voluptuous, standing female nude.

His work sought to amplify and make profound the idea of generation, of creative forces, and human fecundity, embodied in sculptural terms. Certain influential personalities such as the sculptor Daniel Chester French took immediate offense to Lachaise's sculpture, and throughout his life, Lachaise fought against the vilification that was heaped upon him by a conservative public. What Lachaise achieved was a revitalization of figurative sculpture in America, a sculpture which had become a worn-out repetition of stale neo-classicist themes. In his *Standing Woman*, Lachaise brought his great series of figures to its final form, achieving a monumental vitality fully expressed in an organization of forms symbolic of life itself.

511

Reg Butler (*1913)

Girl in Shift   1953-1954
Bronze   H. 66⅛ in. (168 cm)
Gift of Mr. and Mrs. Herbert Rothschild   61.207

This sculpture represents the antithesis of the classical ideal as envisioned by Powers in his *Greek Slave*. It is not a reposed, carefully proportioned, well-modeled, idealized figure, dependent upon an older convention. Instead, Butler, taking liberty with the human form, elongates it for its expressive linear qualities. Rather than mass and volume, propagated so intensely by Lachaise, this figure, planted on thin rods, soars upward, reaching and struggling, yet constricted by a shift.

Butler, a trained architect, gave up this profession in 1950 to devote himself exclusively to sculpture. His early training is reflected in his sculptural preoccupation with points of stress. In 1953, he came to public attention as the recipient of the Grand Prize in the International Sculpture Competition for a monument to the Unknown Political Prisoner.

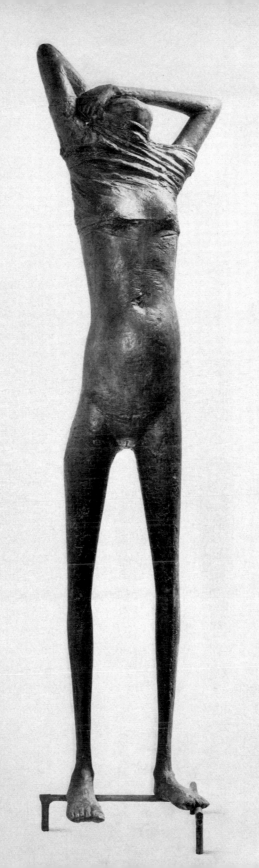

Seymour Lipton
(* 1903)

Earth Forge II   1955
Nickel-silver over steel   H. 31⅛ in. (79.4 cm)
Dick S. Ramsay Fund   56.188

Through a pendulous history of revolutions and counter-revolutions, twentieth-century art has come to encompass forms that faithfully reproduce nature, and others that are unrecognizably abstracted from their source.

Earth Forge, in fact without counterpart in the real world, is reminiscent of elements of both the organic and machine worlds. Seymour Lipton said when recently interviewed on the subject of this work: "The quality of its polarity is a key to a great deal of my thinking ... My involvement and preoccupation is one involving a dynamic interplay between the interior and exterior of reality ... This interior quality has a mystery — it's a darkness, it's a reality. You look at the earth in the winter and what do you see — a barren nothing, but you know through the movement of the sun in the spring, things will happen. This particular work in a sense is a formal projection of one of the areas that I'm concerned with — in the general environment of my life ... Why do I call this work *Earth Forge*? An earth forge is a place where things are being made; not by little men and not by big men, by forces, by processes of nature, and I sense the goings on." Originally working in the more conventional media of wood and stone, Lipton evolved, in the late 1940's, a method which has become his hallmark, the shaping of sheet steel directly followed by melting rods of bronze or nickel silver with an oxyacetylene torch to lend texture and strength.

514

Chronology

1823	The Apprentices Library is formed by several of the leading citizens of Brooklyn at a meeting in Stephenson's Tavern. Library housed on Fulton Street.
1824	The Association is incorporated with the purpose of establishing a library and forming collections in order to enlarge the knowledge and improve the conditions of workers. The Brooklyn Savings Bank is established at a meeting of the Association, and a relationship arranged with the Apprentices Library.
1825	The cornerstone of the new Apprentices Library Building, located at the corner of Henry and Cranberry Streets, is laid by the Marquis de Lafayette.
1828	The Brooklyn City Library is started by members of the Apprentices Library.
1835	Walt Whitman becomes the temporary librarian. Library closes because of lack of interest.
1836	Library building is sold to the City of Brooklyn.
1838	Library reopens. Quarters are rented in the old library building and in the Lyceum Building on Washington Street.
1840	Library reorganized with Augustus Graham as President.
1841	The library section of the organization renamed the Youths' Free Library.
1842	Augustus Graham buys the Lyceum building on Washington Street for the Apprentices Library.
1843	Name of the organization changed to the Brooklyn Institute.
1844	Natural History Department organized.
1846	Permanent gallery of art established.
1852	Augustus Graham, who died in the previous year, leaves a bequest which starts the art school and an art gallery.
1857	The Brooklyn Mercantile Library Association started by members of the Brooklyn Institute. This organization was the predecessor of the Brooklyn Public Library.
1863	The holdings of the Brooklyn City Library are divided between the Brooklyn Institute and the Long Island Historical Society.
1867	Washington Street building undergoes a major remodeling.

1888	Bill is passed in the State Senate stating that certain parts of Prospect Park in the City of Brooklyn would not be sold and could be leased to arts and sciences museums and libraries.
1890	Large fire occurs in the Washington Street building destroying many books and works of art. The remaining collections are stored in nearby institutions, and classes carried on elsewhere. The name of the Brooklyn Institute changed to the Brooklyn Institute of Arts and Sciences.
1891	A bill is passed by the City of Brooklyn to erect a museum building on a Prospect Hill site. Authority is given by the City to lease land to the Brooklyn Institute of Arts and Sciences. The Washington Street building is sold to the City to make way for a Brooklyn Bridge extension.
1891-92	The Mayor and the Commissioner of Parks select the site for the museum building on Prospect Hill.
1892-93	Mayor, Comptroller, and Commissioner of Parks are made ex-officio members of the corporation and the Board of Trustees by an act of legislation. A plan and design for the museum building is secured through competition among architects, and McKim, Mead and White win the contract.
1893-94	The land is leased to the Brooklyn Institute of Arts and Sciences for 100 dollars. The Adams Mansion in Bedford Park is leased to hold the collections until the new building is ready for occupancy.
1895	Contract for erecting the first section of the museum is signed. The land is graded and the ground broken. The cornerstone is laid by Mayor Charles A. Schieren, a trustee and officer of the Institute.
1897	The museum building is officially opened, and the collections are moved to the new site.
1899	The Bedford Park building will be used for a Children's Museum, a branch of the Central Museum.
1901	Libraries at the Central Museum and the Children's Museum are organized and made available to the public.
1905	Central section of the Museum completed.
1906	Front steps and central approach to the building completed.

519

1907	The entire front of the Museum is completed with the exception of the statues.
1908	Library is moved to the east wing basement (now second floor) where it has remained until the present time.
1911	Completion and installation of Japanese and Californian Halls.
1913	Print Department started under the charge of the librarian.
1916	The Wilbour Collection of Egyptian Antiquities and its accompanying library are acquired.
1920	A subway stop opened in front of the building, permitting direct connections to the Museum.
1924	Sections F and G of the Museum completed.
1929	Pipe organ donated to the Museum by Mrs. Edward C. Blum.
1934	The front steps of the Museum are removed. The auditorium is transformed into a new entrance hall which was structually completed. The Natural History Department of the Institute is discontinued, and the collections dispersed.
1935	The new entrance and entrance hall of the Museum are opened. The land in front of the entrance is landscaped.
1936	The new reference room of the Library is opened. Landscaping around the Brooklyn Museum, Botanic Garden, and the Brooklyn Public Library.
1937	The Print Room, a gift as a memorial to William A. Putnam, is received.
1940-41	The Industrial Division is established. The collection of textiles and costumes is made available to the dress and textile designers of the city.
1941-42	Certain objects are evacuated from the Museum's collections because of war. Exhibitions concerning the war are shown. The Art School is moved to the central building.
1943	Material removed during the previous years is returned from the depository.
1945	Reconversion from wartime activities to post-war programs completed.
1948	The Museum obtains the New-York Historical Society's Egyptian collections.

1949	The Community Committee is formally organized.
1951	The first stage of a five-year rehabilitation program for the Museum building is begun. The Edward C. Blum Design Laboratory is established.
1953	The Museum's Egyptian galleries are reopened.
1956	Galleries for Decorative Arts, Watercolors, and Sculpture are reconstructed and reopened.
1958	The Coptic galleries are completed.
1960	The Chinese and Japanese galleries are stripped, re-decorated, and reinstalled.
1961	An orientation program is begun to make visitors aware of the Museum's collections and programs. Information desk and floor plans are installed. Design Department responsible for the appearance of all publications is initiated. Junior Membership program is arranged.
1964	The Jan Martense Schenck House is erected and opened to the public on April 25, 1964. Daniel Chester French's allegorical figures of "Brooklyn" and "Manhattan" placed on either side of the main entrance.
1964-65	The Hall of the Americas is installed in the court on the main floor and opened to the public on May 1, 1965. Excavations at Mendes in the Egyptian Delta are started with success.
1965	A three-hundred car parking lot is opened for business at the rear of the building.
1966	The Frieda Schiff Warburg Memorial Garden is completed in the rear of the Museum. Architectural sculpture from buildings destroyed in the New York area is exhibited.
1967	The first Study Gallery, containing almost 1,000 paintings, is opened on the fifth floor.

Donors, Trustees,
and Staff

DONORS

The quality of The Brooklyn Museum has been determined over the years by the generosity of literally hundreds. Space limitations permit the inclusion of only those whose benefactions have been of a sufficiently high order to warrant one of the higher categories of membership.

Abraham, Abraham
Avery, Samuel P.
Babbott, Frank L.
Babbott, Dr. Frank L., Jr.
Batterman, Henry
Bell, James A. H.
Benson, Frank Sherman
Benson, Miss Mary E.
Blackford, Mrs. Eugene G.
Blashfield, Mrs. Evangeline Wilbour
Bliss, Miss Susan D.
Blum, Edward C.
Blum, Mrs. Edward C.
Blum, John R. H.
Blum, Robert E.
Brackett, George C.
Calverly, William H.
Cary, William H.
Catlin, Mrs. Daniel
Childs, Mrs. William H.
Clement, Arthur W.
Coudert, Mrs. Frederic R., Jr.
Crawford, Morris D. C.
Crawford, Mrs. Morris D. C.
Crittenden, Walter H.
de Menil, Mrs. John
De Silver, Carll H.
Dickerman, Mrs. Watson B.
Doughty, Mrs. Samuel
Draper, Mrs. Mary Childs
Esty, Mrs. William C.
Feder, Mrs. J. Fuller
Filson, Mrs. Ella J.
Fraad, Daniel, Jr.
Friedsam, Col. Michael
Frothingham, Miss Elizabeth W.
Frothingham, John W.
Fuchs, Emil
Gamble, Mrs. Elizabeth Lowe
Garbisch, Mrs. Bernice Chrysler
Garbisch, Col. Edgar W.
Goan, Miss Adelaide

Happel, Lina V.
Harkness, Mrs. Edward S.
Harkness, Miss Mary
Haskell, Mrs. J. Amory
Haslett, Samuel E.
Havemeyer, Horace
Havemeyer, Mrs. Horace
Haynes, Mrs. Stephen B.
Healy, A. Augustus
Hearn, George A.
Hearst, William Randolph, Jr.
Hearst, Mrs. William Randolph, Jr.
Heeren, Rodman A. de
Henderson, Prof. Harold
Herriman, William H.
Hills, Mrs. John
Hoagland, Joseph C.
Hooper, Franklin W.
Howe, Miss Margaret I.
Hoyt, Samuel N.
Hutchins, Waldo, Jr.
James, Mrs. Darwin R. III
Jenkins, Alfred W.
Jones, Frank S.
Kevorkian, Hagop
Ladd, Mrs. William S.
Lester, Mrs. Joseph H.
Lever, H. Randolph
Lewisohn, Adolph
Lewisohn, Sam A.
Lockwood, Luke Vincent
Lockwood, Mrs. Luke Vincent
Loeser, Frederick
Lorimer, Mrs. George Burford
Maddock, Sidney
Martin, Alastair Bradley
Martin, Henry P.
McLean, Matilda
Miles, Mrs. Emily Winthrop
Morrison, Donald S.
Oenslager, Mrs. Donald M.
Olcott, Misses Bianca and Mary

Gould, Edwin
Graef, Edward L.
Graham, Augustus
Polhemus, Mrs. Caroline H.
Pratt, Frederic B.
Pratt, Mrs. Frederic B.
Pratt, George D.
Proctor, Alfred W.
Putnam, William A.
Putnam, Mrs. William A.
Rabinowitz, Louis M.
Ramos, Arturo
Ramos, Paul Peralta
Ramsay, Dick Swift
Rockefeller, John D., Jr.
Rogers, Mrs. Millicent H.
Rothschild, Walter N.
Sanders, Mrs. Frank K., Jr.
Schieren, Hon. Charles A.
Scudder, Hon. Townsend
Sheldon, Henry K.
Simon, Mrs. Leo

Pell, Rev. Alfred Duane
Perkins, Joseph T.
Peters, Mrs. William Sterling
Simpson, Wesley
Stokes, Mrs. S. Emlen
Stutzer, Herman
Szold, Harold J.
Underwood, John T.
Van Sinderen, Adrian
Van Sinderen, Mrs. Adrian
Princess Viggo of Denmark
White, Alfred T.
White, Miss Frances E.
White, Miss Harriet H.
Wiesenberger, Arthur
Wilbour, Charles Edwin
Wilbour, Miss Theodora
Wilbour, Victor
Woodward, Col. Robert B.
Young, Hon. Richard
Zoebisch, Mrs. Alfred T.

DIRECTORS, TRUSTEES,
AND GOVERNORS

527

528

530

THE STAFF

Dates indicate occupancy of professional positions; they do not necessarily show
when a person joined the staff of the Museum.

Abell, Walter (Supervisor of Education) 1937
Abernathy, J. W. (Corr. Secretary, Vice President, President,
Dept. of Philology) 1897-1913
Adam, Tassilo (Assoc. Curator Dept. of Ethnology, Curator of Eastern
and Near Eastern Art) 1929-1933
Adams, Cyrus, C. (Vice President, Dept. of Geography) 1897-1901
Adams, Edward (Auditor) 1899-1906
Aitkin, Helen J. (Cataloguer, Labeler, Asst. Curator Division of
Mollusks) 1899-1922
Allan, Harry (Faculty, Art School) 1951-1961
Allen, Mary W. (Cataloguer Dept. of Libraries) 1904-1911
Alpers, Martin E. (Secretary, Dept. of Microscopy) 1906-1907
Ames, Frank H. (Curator, Secretary, Secretary Section on Conchology,
Dept. of Zoology) 1897-1909
Anderson, Hilda (Instructor) 1955-1957
Antonakos, Stephen (Faculty, Art School) 1965-
Ashby, George E. (President, Vice President, Dept. of Mineralogy,
President, Dept. of Microscopy) 1899-1915
Atkins, Charles D. (Director, Dept. of Education) 1916-1918
Atkinson, Frederick W. (Vice President, Dept. of Political Science) 1904-1918
Averill, Horace P. (Treasurer, Dept. of Photography) 1898-1899
Bageris, John (Faculty, Art School) 1961-1965
Baker, Bertha K. (Vice President, Dept. of Dramatic Art) 1913-1915
Baker, Thomas O. (First Vice President, Dept. of Pedagogy) 1916-1918
Baldwin, William J. (Vice President, Dept. of Engineering) 1908-1918
Bank, Arnold (Faculty, Art School) 1947-1953
Banker, Grace Wood (Librarian, Art Reference Library) 1939-1951
Barber, Joseph (Faculty, Art School) 1961-1962
Barker, Walter (Faculty, Art School) 1963-1966
Barret, Oliver O'Connor (Faculty, Art School) 1950-1955
Barstow, William S. (Vice President, President, Dept. of Electricity) 1897-1901
Bartley, Elias H. (Vice President, Dept. of Chemistry) 1899-1901
Bather, William T. (Vice President, Dept. of Microscopy, Secretary,
Dept. of Mineralogy) 1910-1918
Baumbach, Harold (Faculty, Art School) 1951-1952; 1961-1963
Baur, John I. H. (Acting Supervisor, Supervisor of Education, Curator,
Contemporary Art, Acting Curator Renaissance Art, Curator of
Paintings and Sculpture) 1934-1952
Baumgardt, B. R. (Second Vice President Dept. of Astronomy) 1914-1915
Baziotes, William (Faculty, Art School) 1949-1953
Beason, Ann H. (Instructor) 1963-1966
Beckmann, Max (Faculty, Art School) 1949-1950
Beecher, William C. (Vice President, Dept. of Botany) 1900-1901
Beers, Nathan T. (Vice President, Dept. of Photography) 1908-1909

Behr, Edward A. (Librarian Section on Ornithology Dept. of Zoology) 1897-1904
Bell, James D. (Second Vice President, President Dept. of Law) 1901-1918
Bell, John H. (Taxidermist) 1847
Beller, Florence (Administrative Assistant to Director) 1955-
Bender, John (Carpenter) 1899-1905
Benedict, Robert D. (First Vice President Dept. of Law) 1898-1905
Best, Lyman A. (President Dept. of Entomology) 1897-1910
Beyer, Margaret W. (Asst. Curator Oriental Art) 1948-1949
Bigelow, Margaret D. (Instructor) 1946
Billings, Dorothy (Instructor) 1959-1964
Bindrum, John I. (Faculty, Art School) 1945-1963
Blaustein, Alfred (Faculty, Art School) 1953-1954
Block, Lou (Faculty, Art School) 1948-1951
Boger, William A. (Second Vice President, First Vice President
  Dept. of Photography) 1899-1902
Bohn, Harry G. (Treasurer Dept. of Photography) 1913-1918
Boston, Frederick J. (First Vice President Dept. of Painting) 1897-1909
Boston, Joseph H. (Instructor Evening Art Classes) 1899-1916
Bothmer, Bernard V. (Asst., Assoc. Curator, Curator Ancient Art) 1957-
Botto, Otto (Faculty, Art School) 1948
Boughton, Willis (President Dept. of Philology) 1914-1918
Boulton, Mrs. Alfred J. (Vice President Dept. of Domestic Science) 1906-1918
Bowden, Joseph (President Dept. of Mathematics) 1900-1915
Bowdoin, William G. (Secretary, Vice President
  Dept. of Microscopy) 1897-1903
Boyle, Fred T. L. (Prof. of Architecture) 1872
Brainerd, Edith B. (Secretary Dept. of Botany) 1908-1918
Braislin, William G. (First Vice President Dept. of Zoology) 1900-1907
Braverman, Sylvia (Faculty, Art School) 1949-1951
Breckenridge, Bruce (Faculty, Art School) 1965-
Brewer, John H. (Secretary Dept. of Music) 1897-1918
Bridgham, Emily G. (Recording Secretary Dept. of Philology) 1897-1913
Bridgman, Herbert L. (President Dept. of Geography) 1904-1918
Bristol, Homer C. (Secretary Dept. of Pedagogy) 1901-1911
Brooks, Albert J. (Secretary Dept. of Astronomy, President Dept. of
  Astronomy) 1901-1918
Brown, Alfred H. (President Dept. of Dramatic Art) 1913-1915
Brown, Bernadette (Instructor) 1964-
Bruner, Catherine R. (Senior Docent) 1930-1933
Brussel-Smith, Bernard (Faculty, Art School) 1949-1951
Bryan, Mrs. S. Sheppard (Secretary Dept. of Political Science) 1916-1918
Bryant, William J. (First Vice President Dept. of Photography) 1897-1898
Buechner, Thomas S. (Director of Museum) 1960-
Burdett, Mrs. C. H. (Second Vice President Dept. of Photography,
  Secretary Dept. of Agriculture) 1897-1913
Burns, Jerome (Faculty, Art School) 1960-1961
Burton, Henry C. (First Vice President, Vice President Dept. of Zoology,
  Chairman Section on Ornithology Dept. of Zoology) 1897-1900
Burton, Virginia (Librarian Wilbour Library) 1956-1958
Busa, Peter (Faculty, Art School) 1949-1950

Butterfield, Ramona (Instructor)   1947-1948
Call, R. Elsworth (Second Vice President, Cchairman Section on
    Conchology Dept. of Zoology)   1900-1904
Cameron, Elizabeth (Asst. Librarian & Prints)   1934-1935
Campbell, Rev. Frederick (Vice President, President Dept. of
    Astronomy)   1901-1911
Candell, Victor (Faculty, Art School)   1948-1954
Candler, Flamen B. (President Dept. of Law)   1897-1898
Capart, Jean (Honorary Curator, Assoc. Curator, Advisory Curator of
    Egyptology, Honorary Advisory Curator of Ancient Art)   1932-1945
Capen, Crawford (Vice President, President Section on Philately)   1899-1901
Cappelle, Julie E. (Recording Secretary Dept. of Philology)   1913-1918
Carberry, John D. (Secretary, Treasurer Section on Philately)   1898-1917
Carlsen, Catherine B. (Instructor)   1944-1948
Carly, Henry A. (Curator, Treasurer Dept. of Photography)   1898-1903
Carter, Cynthia R. (Sales Manager)   1937
Carter, Walter S. (President Dept. of Music)   1897-1899
Caruso, T. Anthony (Asst. Curator, Curator Dept. of Photography,
    Photographer)   1946-1954
Casarella, Edmund (Faculty, Art School)   1956-1960
Casey, Thomas F. (Asst. & Clerk, Superintendent of Buildings)   1899-1919
Cavallo, Adolph S. (Curator of American Decorative Arts)   1952-1953
Chadwick, Mrs. Mara P. (President Dept. of Domestic Science)   1902-1903
Chamberlain, Betty (Community Development)   1956-1957
Champman, Allan (In Charge of Catalogue, Library)   1952-1956
Chapin, Henry E. (President Dept. of Botany)   1903-1914
Chase, A. Elizabeth (Curator of Education)   1946-1947
Chase, Louise (Asst. Curator Medieval Art, Asst. Charge of American
    Rooms)   1935-1936
Chatfield, Jennifer (Instructor)   1950-1955
Cherrie, George K. (Taxidermist, Curator of Ornithology)   1899-1911
Chesky, Ruth A. (Asst., Assoc. Photographer)   1958-1966
Churchill, Diane (Instructor)   1966-
Citron, Minna (Faculty, Art School)   1945-1946
Claassen, Arthur (Second Vice President, First Vice President
    Dept. of Music)   1900-1915
Clark, Evelyn (Publicity Secretary to Community Committee,
    Director of Public Relations)   1952-1957
Clark, Josephine A. (Cataloguer)   1889-1890
Clark, Oliver B. (President Dept. of Zoology)   1897-1901
Clendenin, Ida M. (Vice President Dept. of Botany)   1903-1907
Code, Grant (Editor, Curator Dance Center)   1934-1938
Coit, Richard M. (President, Recording Secretary, Secretary Dept. of
    Photography)   1908-1918
Coleman, Roy (Faculty, Art School)   1963-1964
Collins, Lorraine (Asst. Curator Paintings & Sculpture)   1946
Colonna, Roy (Faculty, Art School)   1951-1952
Colson, William B. (Treasurer, President Dept. of Photography)   1899-1904
Congdon, Henry M. (Vice President Dept. of Architecture)   1897-1909
Congdon, Robert W. (Corresponding Secretary Dept. of Photography)   1910-1912

Conklin, Mrs. George W. (President Section on Mycology, Secretary
   Dept. of Botany) 1898-1903
Conover, Robert (Faculty, Art School) 1962-
Conro, Emma O. (Vice President Dept. of Domestic Science) 1900-1907
Conroy, William (Chief Accountant, Bursar Purchasing Agent & Auditor) 1933-1957
Cook, Margaret J. (Asst. Librarian) 1889-1890
Cooney, Andree L. (Acting Asst. Curator Oriental Art) 1958-1962
Cooney, John D. (Registrar, Asst. Curator, Curator of Egyptology,
   Curator of Ancient Art, Curator of Egyptian Art, Acting Director,
   Keeper of the C. E. Wilbour Collection) 1934-1963
Cowdrey, Bartlett (Registrar) 1940-1941
Crandall, Mary I. (Librarian) 1889-1890
Crawford, Elizabeth (Honorary Advisor, Industrial Design & Edward
   C. Blum Design Laboratory) 1946-1963
Crawford, M. D. C. (Honorary Advisor Industrial Division) 1940-1945
Crawford, Ralston (Faculty, Art School) 1948-1950; 1954-1955
Creer, Doris (Instructor) 1958-1963
Creevy, Mrs. Caroline A. (Secretary, President, Vice President
   Dept. of Botany) 1898-1903
Critchley, J. William (Chief Taxidermist) 1902-1909
Cruikshank, James (Vice President Dept. of Mathematics, Vice President,
   Secretary Dept. of Geography) 1897-1916
Crumrine, James (Faculty, Art School) 1960-1962
Culin, Stewart (Curator, President Dept. of Ethnology) 1902-1928
Cummings, Cornelia (Asst. Registrar, Cashier, Registrar) 1901-1918
Cunningham, Francis (Faculty, Art School) 1963-
Daly, Charles P. (Vice President Dept. of Geography) 1897-1899
Daniels, Jean (Asst. Primitive Art Conservation Laboratory) 1962-1963
Danziger, Miriam (Instructor) 1948
Daus, Rudolphe L. (Vice President Dept. of Architecture) 1902-1903
Davenport, Charles (Director Biological Laboratory, President
   Dept. of Zoology, Second Vice President Dept. of Sociology) 1899-1918
Davenport, Mortimer H. (Cataloguer) 1936
Davidson, Patricia F. (Research Associate Ancient Art) 1965-
Davis, Harriet E. (Asst. Registrar) 1914-1918
Day, H. Brooks (Librarian Dept. of Music) 1908-1918
Dayton, Charles A. (Chairman Section on Conchology, Second
   Vice President Dept. of Zoology) 1897-1900
Debevoise, Mr. (Librarian & Janitor) 1835
Dehli, Arne (Vice President, President Dept. of Architecture) 1911-1918
Dekins, Augustus T. (Machinist) 1899-1904
Denny, Charles B. (Vice President Dept. of Photography) 1912-1914
De Wetter, Herman (Photographer, Curator Dept. of Photography) 1934-1948
Diana, Paul (Faculty, Art School) 1946-1947
Dickinson, Edwin (Faculty, Art School) 1949-1958
Dienes, Sari (Faculty, Art School) 1946-1948
Dobbs, John (Faculty, Art School) 1956-1959
Doggett, Allen B. (Second Vice President Dept. of Photography) 1898-1899
Doll, Jacob (Asst. Curator, First Asst. Curator of Entomology
   Curator Division of Lepidotera) 1897-1922

Donaldson, Theodore (Faculty, Art School) 1962-1964
Donlon, Elaine (Membership) 1948-1951
Dorfman, Ethel (Charge of Catalogue Art Reference Library) 1949-1952
Dorward, Mary S. (Asst. Librarian & Prints, Asst. Librarian, Librarian) 1934-1958
Dougherty, J. Hampden (Second Vice President, President Dept. of Law) 1898-1905
Douglas, Alice A. (Secretary Dept. of Zoology) 1897-1899
Douglas, C. H. J. (Secretary Dept. of Political Science) 1897-1901
Douglass, Calvin (Faculty, Art School) 1965-
Doyle, Thomas (Faculty, Art School) 1961-
Drumlevitch, Seymour (Faculty, Art School) 1958-1959
Dubin, Ralph (Faculty, Art School) 1962-1963
Duerden, Lawrence L. (Vice President, Secretary Dept. of Microscopy) 1898-1907
Dunn, Mrs. John K. (President Dept. of Domestic Science) 1897-1902
Dunn, Mrs. W. E. (Secretary Dept. of Agriculture) 1914-1918
Duvinage, Louis (Secretary Dept. of Engineering) 1897-1907
Dyer, Carlus (Faculty, Art School) 1950-1951
Dykeman, Conrad V. (Vice President Dept. of Political Science) 1897-1904
Easby, Elizabeth (Acting Curator Primitive Art and New World Cultures) 1965-
Edsall, James B. (Secretary, Second Vice President Dept. of Pedagogy) 1900-1911
Ehrlich, Pearl (Instructor) 1963-1966
Ehrman, Artis H. (Vice President Dept. of Mineralogy, Vice President,
  President Dept. of Microscopy) 1897-1899
Ekholm, Susanna (Research Asst. Primitive Art and New World
  Cultures) 1963-1965
Eisenhauer, Letty (Faculty, Art School) 1965-
Elliott, Caroline M. (Reference Asst. Library) 1935-1936
Emery, Charles E. (President Dept. of Engineering) 1897-1898
Emlen, Mary C. (Instructor) 1939-1941
Engelhardt, George P. (Asst. in Zoology, Vice President, Secretary
  Dept. of Zoology, Curator Division of Lower Invertebrates,
  Acting Curator, Curator, Honorary Curator Dept. of
  Natural Science, Honorary Curator of Natural History,
  Vice President, Secretary Dept. of Entomology) 1903-1941
Ericson, Laurence (Asst. in Taxidermy) 1899-1905
Fain, Yonia (Faculty, Art School) 1956-
Farquharson, Percy G. (Corresponding Secretary, Vice President
  Dept. of Photography) 1899-1907
Farr, Fred (Faculty, Art School) 1951-1964
Farr, Mabel A. (Asst. Librarian) 1889-1890
Farrar, Preston C. (Vice President Dept. of Philology) 1914-1918
Fay, Charles R. (Secretary Dept. of Political Science) 1912-1915
Fay, Irvin W. (Vice President, President Dept. of Chemistry) 1898-1915
Fayerweather, Eleanor A. (Instructor) -1946
Fazakas, Donelda (Faculty, Art School) 1953-1958
Felter, William L. (President Dept. of Pedagogy) 1897-1918
Ferguson, Frank (Dramatic Director Dept. of Dramatic Art) 1917-1918
Ferguson, James H. (Recording Secretary, Second Vice President
  Dept. of Photography) 1898-1902
Ferree, Barr (President Dept. of Architecture) 1897-1902
Ferren, John (Faculty, Art School) 1946-1951

Finkelstein, Louis (Administrative Asst. Art School)   1951-1956
Fischer, Bernard (Faculty, Art School)   1957-1958
Fisher, George H. (Second Vice President Dept. of Law)   1908-1909
Fletcher, Mary R. (In Charge Loan Division)   1945-1949
Flint, Thomas (Vice President Dept. of Archaeology)   1897-1904
Floyd, Arthur (Faculty, Art School)   1958-1961
Ford, Alice E. (Asst. for Reference & Periodicals)   1937
Forakis, Peter (Faculty, Art School)   1962-1963
Fortess, Karl (Faculty, Art School)   1953-1955
Foss, Glenn (Faculty, Art School)   1948-1950
Fox, Carl (Administrative Asst. Art School, Manager of Gallery Shop)   1951-1964
Fox, Suzanne L. (Registrar)   1952-1955
Fox, William H. (Director)   1914-1933
Fox, Mrs. William H. (Honorary Curator of Lace & Embroidery)   1932-1933
Freeman, Abraham (Asst. Engineer)   1899-1900
French, Delmar (Recording Secretary Dept. of Philosophy, Secretary
   Dept. of Political Science)   1899-1904
Fuller, Charles H. (Vice President Dept. of Political Science)   1913-1918
Gallup, Anna G. (Acting Curator Natural History)   1935
Gardiner, C. Roe (President Dept. of Mineralogy)   1910-1913
Gardner, Augustus H. (Vice President Dept. of Botany)   1899-1900
Garrison, Helen (Asst. Curator Eduction Division & Chairman Junior
   Membership)   1962-1964
Garrison, Jane (Acting Curator Natural History, Secretary to the
   Director)   1936-1940
Giambalvo, Anthony (Conservator, Ancient Art)   1962-1963
Gianakouros, Gregory (Instructor)   1955-1959
Giddings, Franklin H. (President Dept. of Sociology)   1911-1915
Giese, H. E. (Treasurer Classical Section Dept. of Philology)   1897-1898
Gilbert, A. Louise (Librarian Dept. of Astronomy)   1911-1918
Ginnever, Chuck (Faculty, Art School)   1964-
Golding, Grace A. (Administrative Asst. Art School, Registrar
   Art School)   1953-
Goldstein, Julius (Administrative Asst., Faculty Art School)   1958-1965
Gonzalez, Xavier (Faculty, Art School)   1948-1951
Goodwin, Charles T. (Superintendent Museum Buildings)   1899-1903
Goodrich, W. W. (First Vice President Dept. of Law)   1906-1907
Goodyear, William H. (President Dept. of Archaeology, President,
   Curator Dept. of Fine Arts, President & Curator of Fine Arts)   1897-1923
Gordon, John J. (Supervisor of Publications, Secretary, Curator of
   Paintings and Sculpture)   1945-1959
Gottheil, R. J. H. (Vice President, Corresponding Secretary Dept. of
   Philology)   1897-1914
Gottlieb, Ruth (Instructor)   1952-1955
Grabau, Amadeus W. (Vice President Dept. of Geology)   1910-1918
Graef, Edward L. (Curator, President, Honorary Curator Dept. of
   Entomology)   1897-1915
Graham, Augustus (Director)   1823-1825
Graham, John M. (Asst. Curator American Rooms and Textiles,
   Curator American Decorative Arts)   1938-1949

Grant, Alphonsus V. (Chief of Security)   1964-
Gray, J. Newton (Secretary Dept. of Physics)   1911-1913
Grebenak, Louis (Faculty, Art School)   1947-
Greene, Stephen (Faculty, Art School)   1950-1951
Greenlaw, Edwina (Vice President Dept. of Philology)   1910-1914
Griffith, Vincent C. (Vice President Dept. of Architecture)   1898-1901
Griggs, Edward H. (President Dept. of Philosophy)   1904-1918
Grippe, Florence (Faculty, Art School)   1951-1956
Groom, Wallace P. (Asst. Treasurer)   1899-1914
Gross, Chaim (Faculty, Art School)   1945-1946
Grout, Abel J. (Curator, President, Vice President Dept. of Botany)   1898-1914
Gutterman, Siegfried R. (Faculty, Art School)   1945-1946
Gutzmer, Alfred (Faculty, Art School)   1948-1961
Hagar, Stansbury (Secretary Dept. of Archaeology, Secretary,
    President Dept. of Ethnology)   1897-1918
Hall, Rev. Charles H. (President Dept. of Botany)   1890-1897
Hall, James P. (Secretary Dept. of Astronomy)   1897-1898
Hamblet, James (President Dept. of Electricity)   1897-1899
Hancock, William J. (Vice President Dept. of Chemistry)   1901-1911
Hanft, William (Conservator Prints & Drawings)   1962-
Hansen, Charles (Carpenter-Foreman, Chief Carpenter)   1941-1966
Hansen, Donald P. (Consultant Ancient Art)   1963-1964
Hantman, Murray (Faculty, Art School)   1959-
Happel, Theodore W. C. (Librarian Section on Philately)   1901-1902
Harris, Mrs. Isaac (Vice President, President Dept. of Botany)   1901-1903
Harrison, John A. (Engineer, Asst. Engineer)   1899-1906
Hart, Lewis T. (Engineer, Chief Engineer, Business Manager)   1900-1933
Hart, Robert G. (Editor)   1960-1961
Hartl, Leon (Faculty, Art School)   1946-1948
Hartmann, Wolfgang (Photographer)   1963-
Hartt, Margaret V. (Asst. Curator & Chairman Junior Membership
    Education Division)   1965-1966
Hatch, Charles L. (Secretary Dept. of Mineralogy)   1897-1905
Hausmann, Hubert S. (Vice President Dept. of Electricity)   1910-1918
Hawes, Edward S. (Chairman Classical Section Dept. of Philology)   1897-1898
Hawn, Henry G. (Vice President Dept. of Dramatic Art)   1913-1915
Hayden, Robert J. (Superintendent)   1966-
Haynes, Elizabeth (Asst. Curator Dept. of Decorative Arts,
    Asst. Curator of American Rooms)   1928-1935
Hebald, Milton (Faculty, Art School)   1946-1953
Heinze, Louise (Cataloguer)   1937
Henderson, E. N. (Corresponding Secretary Dept. of Philosophy)   1902-1903
Hendrick, Robert E. P. (Asst. Curator Decorative Arts)   1966-
Henricksen, Albert N. (Superintendent, Acting Director,
    Asst. to Director)   1934-1963
Henshaw, Frederick V. (Secretary Dept. of Electricity)   1899-1907
Hewlett, J. Monroe (Vice President, President Dept. of Architecture)   1901-1912
Henrichs, Frederick W. (Second Vice President, President Dept. of Law)   1897-1900
Hitz, Joseph L. (Recording Secretary Dept. of Photography)   1900-1907
Hoagland, Susan W. (Secretary Dept. of Sociology)   1911-1914

Hobson, G. P. F. (Secretary Classical Section Dept. of Philology)   1897-1898
Hochfield, Sylvia (Editor)   1966-
Hofsted, Jolyon (Faculty, Art School)   1964-
Holden, Samuel (President Dept. of Photography)   1904-1907
Holian, Grace O. (Registrar)   1936-1940
Holland, Alexander (Treasurer, Vice President Section on Philately)   1898-1904
Hooper, Franklin W. (Director)   1899-1914
Hooper, Mrs. Franklin W. (Secretary, Vice President Dept. of
    Domestic Science)   1897-1918
Hooper, John (Actuary and Librarian)   1854
Hoopes, Donelson F. (Assoc. Curator, Curator Paintings & Sculpture)   1965-
Hopkins, Albert A. (Secretary Dept. of Fine Arts)   1902-1909
Hotaling, Charles (Printer)   1901-1905
Howeel, Arthur H. (Curator, Section on Ornithology Dept. of Zoology) 1897-1899
Howland, Margaret (Instructor)   1946-1948
Hui Ka Kwong (Faculty, Art School)   1952-1960
Hulst, George D. (President Dept. of Botany, Librarian Dept. of
    Entomology)   1897-1900
Hultberg, Paul (Faculty, Art School)   1952-1953
Hunt, Joseph H. (Curator Dept. of Botany, Secretary Dept. of
    Ethnology)   1897-1907
Huntington, Frederick W. (Secretary Dept. of Physics)   1917-1918
Hutchinson, Susan A. (Curator of Books, Librarian, Curator of
    Prints and Librarian)   1899-1934
Hutchinson, William M. (President Dept. of Chemistry)   1897-1899
Hyatt, Thaddeus P. (President, Vice President, Section on Philately,
    Librarian Section on Philately)   1898-1918
Ihlseng, Magnus C. (President Dept. of Engineering)   1914-1918
Ingerham, H. C. M. (Second Vice President Dept. of Law)   1900-1901
Iriberry, Mildred G. (Charge of Loan Room-Education Division,
    Supervisor of Lending Services)   1955-
Jacobowitz, Arlene (Curatorial Asst. Paintings & Sculpture, Asst.
    Curator Paintings & Sculpture)   1963-
Jacobs, Mrs. Andrew (Vice President Dept. of Domestic Science)   1897-1904
Jacobs, Olin M. (Secretary Dept. of Physics)   1913-1914
Jacobson, Albert (Faculty, Art School)   1951-1955
Jelliffe, Cameron (Instructor)   1946-1947
Jenkins, A. S. (Secretary Classical Section Dept. of Philology)   1898-1900
Jervis, Perlee V. (Librarian, First Vice President, Second Vice President
    Dept. of Music)   1897-1918
Jones, Myers R. (Vice President Dept. of Photography)   1916-1918
Johnson, Mildred (Asst. Editor)   1936
Johnson, Una E. (Asst. Library, Asst. Curator, Curator of
    Prints & Drawings)   1936-
Judd, Donald (Faculty, Art School)   1962-1964
Judy, Herbert B. (See Tshudy, Herbert B.)
Jupe, Margaret (Librarian for Reference Art Reference Library)   1958-1960
Kadish, Ruben (Faculty, Art School)   1960-1961
Kaplan, Flora S. (Acting Curator Primitive Art and
    New World Cultures)   1955-1957

542

Kates, George M. (Curator Oriental Art) 1946-1948
Kato, Frederick (Vice President Dept. of Mineralogy) 1901-1907
Katz, Alex (Faculty, Art School) 1959-1960
Katz, Lois (Instructor, Asst. to Curator Education Division, Asst.
 Curator, Assoc. Curator Oriental Art) 1952-
Keck, Caroline (Advisor to Restorer, Consulant Restorer, Conservator,
 Consultant Conservator) 1943-1965
Keck, Sheldon (Restorer, Conservator, Consultant Conservator) 1934-1961; 1965-
Keith, Jean L. (Curatorial Asst., Asst. Curator Ancient Art) 1964-
Kellogg, Brainerd (President Dept. of Philology) 1897-1907
Kelly, James H. (Treasurer Dept. of Photography) 1903-1909
Kelly, Joan H. (Cataloguer Art Reference Library) 1958-1961
Kemp, James S. (President Dept. of Geography) 1897-1900
Kemp, Marilyn E. (Registrar) 1955-1961
Kent, Mrs. E. M. (Registrar & Cashier) 1899-1912
Kent, James W. (Curator, Treasurer, Corresponding Secretary Dept. of
 Photography) 1897-1913
Key-Oberg, Rolf (Faculty, Art School) 1952-1955
Khouri, Laurice (Cataloguer Art Reference Library) 1964-
Kienbusch, William (Faculty, Art School) 1948-
King, Albert E. (Treasurer Dept. of Pedagogy) 1914-1918
King, Cyrus A. (President, Vice President Dept. of Botany) 1914-1918
King, William (Faculty, Art School) 1958-1960
Kingsley, Clarence (Secretary Dept. of Pedagogy) 1911-1913
Kneeland, S. F. (Second Vice President Dept. of Painting) 1897-1915
Knight, Henry C. (Corresponding Secretary Dept. of Photography) 1900-1902
Konrad, Anton (Consultant in Charge Primitive Art Conservation
 Laboratory) 1963-1964
Koch, John (Faculty, Art School) 1963-1964
Kohl, Lynn P. (Asst. Curator Education Division, Chairman Junior
 Membership) 1966-
Kohn, Gabriel (Faculty, Art School) 1959-1960
Kokis, George (Faculty, Art School) 1961-1964
Knox, William T. (Corresponding Secretary Dept. of Photography) 1908-1909
Konzal, Joseph (Faculty, Art School) 1949-
Kouwenhoven, William B. (Vice President Dept. of Electricity) 1908-1909
Krenbiel, Christine (Stylist) 1934
Kreisberg, Irving (Faculty, Art School) 1956-1957
Kriehn, George (Secretary Dept. of Fine Arts) 1910-1917
Kruse, Alexander (Faculty, Art School) 1946-1952
Kurland, Sidney (Graphic Designer) 1962-1964
Landis, Bena (Faculty, Art School) 1952-1953
Lang, William (President Dept. of Microscopy, Secretary Dept. of
 Psychology) 1897-1899
La Salle, Barbara S. (Registrar) 1963-
Latham, John (Supervisor Public Relations) 1958-1961
Lawton, William C. (Vice President Dept. of Philology) 1897-1902
Le Beck, Suzanne (Registrar) (Married — see Fox) 1951-1952
Lee, George J. (Curator Oriental Art) 1948-1959
Leefe, Miriam Kraft (Instructor) 1949-1951

Leeming, Woodruff (Secretary Dept. of Architecture) 1897-1917
Levermore, Charles H. (Vice President Dept. of Political Science) 1897-1913
Levine, David (Faculty, Art School) 1962-1965
Levison, Wallace G. (Curator, Secretary Dept. of Physics, President
Dept. of Microscopy, President Dept. of Mineralogy,
Secretary Dept. of Geology) 1897-1917
Le Vita, David (Musicologist) 1941-1945; 1947-
Lewis, Frederick Z. (Treasurer Dept. of Botany) 1901-1902
Lewis, Nelson P. (Vice President, President Dept. of Engineering) 1903-1914
Libhart, Myles (Supervisor Special Installations Publications, Graphic
Design) 1960-1963
Lloyd, Richard L. (Asst. Dramatic Director Dept. of Dramatic Art) 1916-1917
Longo, Vincent (Faculty, Art School) 1955-1956
Lord, Sheridan N. (Administrative Asst., Faculty Art School) 1963-
Low, J. Herbert (President Dept. of Political Science) 1908-1918
Lowell, Sidney V. (First Vice President, Second Vice President
Dept. of Law) 1905-1918
Lucas, Frederic A. (Curator-In-Chief, Honorary Curator of Natural
Science) 1911-1928
Ludlow, Francis H. (Secretary Dept. of Political Science) 1903-1912
Lumpkin, Audrey (Asst. Bursar) 1941-1944
Luqueer, Frederick L. (Vice President Dept. of Psychology) 1901-1915
Lust, Elenor (Faculty, Art School) 1947-1948
Luther, Agnes V. (Secretary Dept. of Microscopy) 1908-1918
Lyon, Charles W. Jr. (Vice President, President Dept. of Mathematics) 1897-1900
McAllister, Gertrude (Publicity) 1951-1954
McAndrew, William A. (Second Vice President Dept. of Pedagogy,
President Dept. of Geography) 1897-1903
McCabe, James J. (President Dept. of Mathematics) 1902-1903
McDuffie, Sarah (Charge of Catalogue Art Reference Library) 1956-1958
McElroy, Samuel (Vice President Dept. of Engineering) 1897-1898
McEvoy, Michael (Managing Editor) 1963-1965
McGeorge, John (Librarian-Janitor) 1855-1861
McHale, Sally (Membership-Publications, Membership, Asst. Registrar) 1952-
McKay, John S. (President Dept. of Physics, Curator of Physical
Sciences) 1897-1911
McKeen, Hon. James (Second Vice President Dept. of Law) 1910-1911
Macnaughton, William E. (Corresponding Secretary, President Dept. of
Photography) 1903-1918
Macvannel, John A. (Secretary Dept. of Psychology, Corresponding
Secretary Dept. of Philosophy) 1899-1901
Maddren, Mrs. William (Corresponding Secretary Dept. of Photography) 1897-1898
Malteruo, Katherine (Cataloguer-Library) 1936
Mangini, George (Manager Gallery Shop) 1964-
Marsciano, Nicholas (Faculty, Art School) 1949-1956
Martin, Charles (Faculty, Art School) 1965-1966
Martin, Charles C. (Vice President Dept. of Engineering) 1898-1903
Martin, Daniel S. (Curator Dept. of Geology) 1897-1899
Martin, David Stone (Faculty, Art School) 1947-1948
Marvel, Josiah P. (Executive Asst. to Director) 1930-1931

Mathieu, James A. (Faculty, Art School)   1949-1951
Mavros, Donald (Faculty, Art School)   1962-1965
Mayer, Alfred G. (Curator, Honorary Curator of Natural Science,
   President Dept. of Zoology)   1899-1923
Mayhew, Richard (Faculty, Art School)   1963-
Mazzucchi, Edward (Faculty, Art School)   1947-1948
Meeske, Herman (Asst. Curator Dept. of Entomology)   1897-1900
Meleney, Clarence P. (Second Vice President Dept. of Pedagogy)   1916-1918
Melish, Rev. J. Howard (First Vice President Dept. of Sociology)   1912-1918
Melvin, Floyd J. (Secretary Dept. of Sociology)   1916-1918
Merwin, Almon G. (President Dept. of Psychology)   1897-1901
Mickleborough, John (President Dept. of Geology)   1897-1918
Milford, Vivian (Instructor Junior Membership)   1963-1965
Miller, E. Jo (Research Asst., Asst. Curator Prints & Drawings)   1961-
Miller, Hugh (Faculty, Art School)   1960-
Miller, Thomas I. (Vice President, President Dept. of Microscopy)   1903-1915
Minaldi, David (Librarian Section on Philately)   1902-1903
Minick, A. Rachel (Charge of Catalogue Art Reference Library)   1947-1949
Miranda, Antonio (Modeller)   1910-1937
Mofchum, Gerald (Faculty, Art School)   1957-1963
Montgomery, Nina (Instructor)   1945-1946
Montgomery, Robert B. (Vice President Dept. of Photography)   1910-1912
Montgomery, W. B. (First Vice President Dept. of Agriculture)   1912-1915
Moor, Arthur P. (Curator of Education, Supervisor Art School,
   Supersivor of Sunday Programs)   1944-1945
Moore, Eleanor M. (Advisor Education Division)   1944
Moriarty, Mrs. Anne B. (Third Vice President Dept. of Sociology)   1912-1913
Morris, Edward L. (Curator Dept. of Natural Science,
   Acting Curator-In-Chief)   1907-1913
Morris, Mary B. (Docent)   1914-1917
Morse, Charles H. (President Dept. of Photography, First Vice President
   Dept. of Music)   1897-1900
Muir, Mrs. John (Vice President Dept. of Domestic Science)   1897-1900
Mullen, Albert (Faculty, Art School)   1954-1955
Munday, Dale J. (Administrative Asst., Faculty Art School)   1960-1963
Mura, Frank (Museum Guide and Instructor)   1921-1922
Murphy, Michelle (Docent, Advisor Education Division, Educational
   Supervisor, Curator Industrial Division, Research Consultant
   Edward C. Blum Design Laboratory, Curator of American and
   European Costumes)   1934-1954
Murphy, Robert C. (Curator Division of Mammals and Birds,
   Acting Curator, Curator of Natural Sciences)   1911-1920
Mylonas, Eunice (Instructor)   1958-1961
Nagel, Charles (Director of Museum, Curator American Decorative Arts) 1946-1955
Nardin, Warren (Faculty, Art School)   1949-1951; 1955-1956
Nichols, O. F. (President Dept. of Engineering)   1897-1907
Niisuma, Minoru (Faculty, Art School)   1964
Nilsson, Janet T. (Loan Division)   1944
Norris, John H. (Treasurer Dept. of Photography)   1897-1898
Northrop, Henry E. (Secretary Dept. of Geography)   1899-1900

Novak, Barbara (Instructor)   1951-1952
Odate, Toshio (Faculty, Art School)   1962-
Oldenburg, Peter (Faculty, Art School)   1949-1951
O'Leary, William (Secretary Dept. of Geography)   1901-1907
Orr, Mary E. (Third Vice President Dept. of Sociology)   1911-1912
Osborn, Frederick W. (Vice President Dept. of Philosophy,
    Vice Presidet Dept. of Psychology)   1897-1914
Osver, Arthur (Faculty, Art School)   1948-1951
Paine, Charles F. (Corresponding Secretary Dept. of Photography)   1898-1899
Palmer, Mary M. (Second Vice President, Secretary Dept. of
    Agriculture)   1912-1914
Park, James H. (Secretary Dept. of Chemistry)   1897-1918
Parker, De Witt L. (First Vice President Dept. of Photography)   1898-1899
Parker, Hershel (Vice President Dept. of Geography)   1913-1917
Pattison, Robert J. (Third Vice President Dept. of Painting)   1897-1900
Pearsall, Richard F. (Vice President Dept. of Entomology)   1898-1911
Peck, Augustus H. (Supervisor of Art School)   1945-
Peckham, William C. (Vice President Dept. of Physics, President
    Dept. of Photography)   1897-1909
Pell, Rev. Alfred Duane (Vice President Dept. of Fine Arts)   1902-1918
Perkins, Fanny D. (Secretary Dept. of Domestic Science)   1908-1918
Perkins, Mrs. Frank K. (President Dept. of Domestic Science)   1916-1918
Perlin, Bernard (Faculty, Art School)   1947-1948
Perry, Arthur C. (Vice President Dept. of Astronomy)   1897-1901
Peterdi, Gabor (Faculty, Art School)   1948-1954
Peters, Clayton A. (President Dept. of Agriculture)   1912-1918
Picken, George (Faculty, Art School)   1945-1949
Pleasants, Frederick R. (Asst. Curator Primitive Art and New World
    Cultures, Curator Primitive Art and New World Cultures,
    Consultant Primitive Art and New World Cultures)   1948-1959
Pollard, Charles L. (President Dept. of Enthomology)   1911-1915
Pond, Barbara (Registrar)   1945-1951
Powell, Jane (See Jane Powell Rosenthal)
Pratt, Frederic B. (Second Vice President Dept. of Sociology)   1911-1913
Prescott, Alberta P. (Loan Division, Registrar)   1941-1943
Presser, Josef (Faculty, Art School)   1947-1948
Prestopino, Gregorio (Faculty, Art School)   1946-1953
Proctor, Thomas (Vice President Dept. of Botany)   1898-1899
Proetz, Victor (Consultant-Installation)   1949-1954
Quinby, Frank H. (Vice President Dept. of Architecture)   1910-1911
Rattner, Abraham (Faculty, Art School)   1948-1950
Raymond, Joseph H. (Vice President Dept. of Botany)   1897-1898
Raymond, Rossiter W. (Vice President Dept. of Geology)   1897-1909
Redfield, William C. (President Dept. of Music)   1899-1901
Reed, Graham (Second Vice President Dept. of Music)   1916-1918
Renouf, Edda (Docent)   1936-1937
Rexford, F. A. (Secretary Dept. of Botany)   1903-1904
Riefstahl, Elizabeth (Asst. Librarian, Librarian Wilbour Library,
    Asst. Curator of Ancient Art, Assoc. Curator Emeritus Ancient Art,
    Editor)   1937-

546

Riley, John Robert (Acting Consultant, Consultant Industrial Division —
　　Edward C. Blum Design Laboratory, Acting Curator, Curator
　　American and European Costumes, Consultant to the Design
　　Laboratory) 1953-1966
Ring, George W. (Curator, Librarian Section on Philately) 1898-1918
Rittenhouse, H. O. (President, Secretary Dept. of Mathematics) 1903-1916
Roberts, Laurance P. (Curator Oriental Art, Museum Director) 1934-1944
Roberts, Mrs. Laurance P. (Acting Director) 1944-1946
Robinson, Harry E. (Vice President Section on Philately) 1901-1903
Robus, Hugo (Faculty, Art School) 1955-1957
Rockwell, Robert H. (Chief Taxidermist) 1911-1922
Rogalski, Walter (Faculty, Art School) 1953-1957
Rogers, Allen (Vice President Dept. of Chemistry) 1911-1917
Root, Cynthia (Sales Manager) 1936
Rose, Hanna T. (Docent Dept. of Education, Loan Room, Asst. to the
　　Supervisor-Education Dept., Asst. in Charge of Special Events,
　　Supervisor Music Division, Curator of Education Division) 1931-
Rose, I. N. (Librarian) 1870-1871
Rosenblatt, Leon (Conservator Primitive Art and New World Cultures) 1962-
Rosenfeld, Lois Glantz (Registrar) 1958-1961
Rosenthal, Jane Powell (Asst. Curator, Curator Primitive Art and
　　New World Cultures) 1957-
Ross, Gregory (Secretary, Art School) 1945-1950
Ross, Marvin C. (Advisor Medieval Art) 1934-1937
Roston, Arnold (Faculty, Art School) 1950-1951
Rothe, William G. (Vice President, President Dept. of Mineralogy) 1899-1910
Rueff, Andre E. (Asst. Curator of Fine Arts, Acting Curator of
　　Decorative Arts) 1912-1933
Ruprecht, A. C. (Recording Secretary) 1897-1898
Russel, Isaac F. (First Vice President Dept. of Law) 1897-1898
Sabo, Irving (Faculty, Art School) 1952-1955
Sack, Susanne (Asst., Acting Conservator, Conservator) 1960-
Saldern, Axel von (Curator of Paintings & Sculpture, Editor) 1961-1966
Saltonstall, David (Asst. to the Director & Supervisor Public Relations) 1961-
Samenfeld, Lillian (Faculty, Art School) 1963-1965
Samenfeld, Mark (Asst. Supervisor, Faculty Art School) 1956-
Sammis, Elmer G. (Secretary Dept. of Law) 1897-1918
Sanders, Helene (Faculty, Art School) 1945-1946
Sanford, John A. (Vice Chairman Classical Section Dept. of Philology) 1898-1901
Sargent, William D. (President Dept. of Electricity) 1901-1905
Saulpaugh, Dassah (Conservator Decorative Arts and Edward C. Blum
　　Design Laboratory, Assoc. Curator Decorative Arts,
　　Costumes & Textiles) 1962-
Savage, A. D. (Asst. Curator Dept. of Fine Arts) 1907-1912
Schaeffer, Carl (Asst., Assoc. Curator of Entomology, Assoc. Curator
　　Division of Insects other than Lepidoptera) 1902-1922
Schanker, Louis (Faculty, Art School) 1945-1946; 1951-1954
Schardt, Bernard (Faculty, Art School) 1950-1951
Scheinin, Margaret (Instructor) 1947-1950
Schenck, Edgar C. (Director of Museum) 1955-1959

Schiffleger, Carol (Instructor) 1961-1963
Schimpf, Henry W. (Vice President Dept. of Chemistry) 1897-1898
Schniewind, Carl O. (Librarian and Curator of Prints, Acting Curator
    Mediaeval Art) 1935-1938
Schoonhoven, John (Vice President Dept. of Entomology, President
    Dept. of Zoology & Microscopy) 1904-1918
Schoonhoven, Mrs. John J. (President Dept. of Domestic Science) 1903-1915
Schroeder, Frances (Vice President Dept. of Domestic Science) 1904-1905
Schwartz, Manfred (Faculty, Art School) 1947-
Schwartz, Marvin D. (Curator American Decorative Arts, Curator
    Decorative Arts, Editor, Curator, Edward C. Blum Design
    Laboratory) 1953-
Scott, Sarah E. (First Vice President Dept. of Pedagogy, Secretary
    Dept. of Psychology) 1897-1913
Scrimgeour, A. C. (Vice President Dept. of Photography) 1902-1904
Seaver, Benjamin F. (Secretary Dept. of Geography) 1908-1918
Sebert, William F. (Secretary Dept. of Astronomy) 1898-1901
Seebeck, Joseph (Superintendent, Custodian) 1933-
Seewald, Joseph H. (Registrar, Art School) 1950-1951
Seiberling, Cecile (Library Secretary, Asst. Curator Prints and
    Drawings) 1936-1941
Seide, Charles (Faculty, Art School) 1947-1957
Seidenberg, William (Chief Printer) 1934-
Seitz, Irma (Faculty, Art School) 1964-1965
Seldner, Rudolph (Secretary Dept. of Physics) 1897-1911
Serra, Florence (Faculty, Art School) 1946-1947
Serra-Badue, Daniel (Faculty, Art School) 1962-
Servis, Garrett P. (President, Vice President Dept. of Astronomy) 1897-1915
Seymour, John (Chief Engineer) 1934-1936
Shahn, Ben (Faculty, Art School) 1950-1952
Shallow, Edward B. (Secretary, President Dept. of Geography) 1900-1914
Shapiro, Rose B. (Librarian-Wilbour Library) 1960-1963
Sharpe, Richard W. (President Dept. of Microscopy, Vice President
    Dept. of Zoology) 1908-1912
Sheldon, Rufus (President, Vice President Dept. of Mathematics) 1897-1901
Sheldon, Samuel (Vice President, President Dept. of Electricity) 1899-1918
Sherwood, Herbert F. (President Dept. of Sociology) 1916-1918
Shulman, Morris (Faculty, Art School) 1949-1960
Simon, Sidney (Faculty, Art School) 1949-1951; 1955-1956
Singer, Malvin (Faculty, Art School) 1948-1952
Sloan, Cyril (Faculty, Art School) 1946-1947
Skrzyneki, Gustav A. (Secretary Dept. of Architecture) 1901-1902
Smith, Charles J. (Supervising Clerk) 1962-
Smith, Lucilla E. (Secretary Dept. of Botany) 1897-1898
Snyder, William H. (Recording Secretary Dept. of Painting) 1897-1904
Sonin, Robert S. (Asst. Curator Primitive Art and
    New World Cultures) 1963-1966
Soyer, Isaac, (Faculty, Art School) 1947-
Spinden, Herbert (Curator Dept. of Ethnology, Director of Education,
    Curator Prehistoric and Primitive Art, Curator American Indian Art

548

and Primitive Cultures, Curator of Primitive and New World
Cultures, Curator Emeritus Primitive and New World Cultures) 1929
Squier, Frank (President Dept. of Painting, Vice President Dept. of
   Ethnology) 1897-1909
Stabler, Caroline M. (Reference Asst. — Library) 1934
Starr, Theodore D. Jr. (Editor) 1939-1943
Stevens, Anthony (Administrative Asst. Art School) 1953-1957
Stoller, Erica (Asst. Consultant Primitive Art Conservation Laboratory) 1963-1964
Stout, Horace P. (Recording Secretary Dept. of Photography) 1910-1912
Summers, Carol (Faculty, Art School) 1954-1955
Sussmann, Nan (Librarian Wilbour Library) 1963-1966
Sweet, Frederick A. (Curator Renaissance Art) 1934-1935
Swenson, Eleanor B. (Asst. Curator Paintings & Sculpture) 1941-1945
Taft, Mary N. (Secretary Section on Mycology) 1898
Taggart, Edwin L. M. (Asst. Curator of Egyptology) 1932-1935
Taggart, Ralph C. (Secretary Dept. of Engineering) 1910-1914
Talbot, Henry A. (President, Vice President, Treasurer Section on
   Philately) 1899-1918
Tamayo, Rufino (Faculty, Art School) 1946-1948
Tam, Reuben (Faculty, Art School) 1947-
Tanier, Inger (Asst. Curator Costumes, Asst. Curator Edward C. Blum
   Design Laboratory) 1958-1962
Tarbell, Gage E. (Second Vice President Dept. of Agriculture) 1913-1915
Taylor, Bric (Faculty, Art School) 1961-1962
Taylor, Dare (Instructor) 1957-1958
Taylor, John A. (President Dept. of Political Science) 1897-1908
Taylor, William J. (Secretary, Vice President Dept. of Psychology) 1913-1918
Thomas, Gordon (Chief Engineer) 1937-
Thompson, Claire de Kay (Instructor) 1944
Thompson, E. Francis (Faculty, Art School) 1958
Touster, Irwin (Faculty, Art School) 1951-1952
Townsend, Mr. Blanche (Secretary Dept. of Dramatic Art) 1913-1916
Townsend, Charlotte (Instructor) 1948-1953
Tricarico, Dorothy (Asst. Curator Edward C. Blum Design Laboratory,
   Asst. Curator Costumes, Asst. Curator Decorative Arts) 1953-
Tshudy, Herbert B. (Cataloguer and Attendant, Artist, Curator
   Paintings and Sculpture, Curator Contemporary Arts) 1899-1935
Tucker, Samuel M. (President Dept. of Dramatic Art) 1917-1918
Tudor, Charles (Faculty, Art School) 1948-1949
Turner, Grace (Asst. Librarian — Dept. of Prints, Asst. Librarian for
   Reference) 1934-1937
Turner, Margaret C. (Asst. Registrar & Treasurer's Clerk, Accountant) 1899-1918
Tuthill, Lewis H. (Vice President Dept. of Psychology) 1916-1918
Tuttle, Arthur S. (Secretary Dept. of Engineering) 1908-1918
Uber, Cornelia (Instructor) 1966-
Uht, Charles (Photographer) 1956-1963
Underhill, Henry L. (First Vice President, President Dept. of
   Photography) 1899-1900
Untracht, Oppi (Faculty, Art School) 1959-1964
Urban, William Jr. (Treasurer, President Dept. of Mineralogy) 1897-1901

Utter, H. L. (Secretary Section on Ornithology Dept. of Zoology)   1899-1900
Vaill, Margaret (Asst. Designer Installations Publications and Graphic
    Design)   1962-
Van Vleck, Elizabeth (Membership Secretary)   1931-1933
Van Vliet, Alice (Vice Chairman, Secretary Classical Section Dept. of
    Philology)   1897-1901
Verfenstein, Gladys (Cataloguer)   1911-1912
Von Nardroff, Ernest R. (President, Vice President Dept. of Physics)   1910-1918
Waldman, Diane (Faculty, Art School)   1965-1966
Waldman, Paul (Faculty, Art School)   1963-
Walker, Arthur H. (Registrar)   1961-1962
Walker, James (Curator, Treasurer Dept. of Mineralogy, Curator
    Dept. of Microscopy)   1897-1917
Walker, William B. (Librarian Wilbour Library and Art Reference
    Library)   1958-1964
Warner, Edwin G. (Chairman Classical Section Dept. of Philology)   1898-1901
Washburn, Elizabeth (Instructor)   1937-1941
Way, B. G. (Librarian, Secretary Dept. of Astronomy)   1897-1918
Wedge, Eleanor F. (Wilbour Librarian)   1966-
Weed, Henry T. (Secretary Dept. of Electricity)   1897-1899
Weeks, Archibald (Secretary Dept. of Entomology)   1897-1913
Wegener, Hertha (Asst. Curator Paintings & Sculpture)   1947-1962
Weissberg, Robert (Faculty, Art School)   1950-1952
Wells, David S. (Vice President, President Section on Philately)   1898-1900
Wheat, Silas C. (President, Vice President Dept. of Microscopy,
    Librarian Dept. of Enthomology, Vice President, Secretary,
    Dept. of Zoology)   1910-1918
White, Ernest (Organist)   1939-1940
White, Ian M. (Asst. Supervisor, Supervisor, Architectural Installations,
    Supervisor Installations, Publications and Graphic Designs, Supervisor
    Installations and Graphic Designs, Superintendent, Asst. Director   1960-1966
White, La Selle H. (President Dept. of Psychology, Secretary, Second
    Vice President Dept. of Pedagogy)   1897-1918
White, Rev. William T. (First Vice President Dept. of Sociology)   1911-1912
Whiting, Lucille (Reference Librarian)   1960-1962
Whitman, Walter (Acting Librarian)   1855
Willard, Franka (Librarian Dept. of Entomology)   1898-1909
Williams, Mary T. (Secretary to Director — Charge of Publications)   1941-1944
Wilson, Michelle (Asst. Librarian)   1951-1958
Winslow, Margaret S. (Secretary Dept. of Philosophy)   1910-1918
Wing, Henry T. (Second Vice President Dept. of Law)   1911-1918
Wintringham, J. P. (Vice President Dept. of Electricity, President
    Dept. of Microscopy, Secretary Dept. of Mathematics, Curator,
    President Dept. of Mineralogy)   1897-1917
Wolff, Bernard (Graphic Designer)   1964-
Wolins, Joseph (Faculty, Art School)   1961-1962
Wollny, Arthur J. (Asst. Bursar, Bursar, Accountant, Senior Accountant)   1948-
Wood, George C. (Vice President Dept. of Botany)   1914-1918
Woodman, R. Huntington (Acting President, President, First Vice
    President, Second Vice President Dept. of Music)   1897-1918

Woods, Theodora (Cataloguer)	1934-1937
Woodward, Paul J. (Acting Curator Dept. of Fine Arts, Curator Dept. of Decorative Arts)	1924-1927
Woolley, Patricia (Registrar)	1943-1944
Worthington, Erastus (Librarian)	1823
Wright, Judith (Instructor)	1948-1949
Wright, Milton (Faculty, Art School)	1959-
Wyckoff, A. E. (Vice President Dept. of Psychology)	1897-1901
Wynkoop, Herbert S. (Vice President, Secretary Dept. of Electricity)	1903-1918
Young, Curtis C. (Second Secretary of Ornithology Dept. of Zoology)	1897-1899
Young, Dona (Instructor Junior Membership)	1962-1963
Young, Gertrude M. (Docent, Museum Guide and Instructor, Acting Asst. Curator of Fine Arts)	1919-1924
Young, Mabela (Secretary Dept. of Botany)	1904-1905
Youtz, Philip N. (Director of Museums)	1934-1940
Zabriskie, J. L. (Vice President Dept. of Entomology)	1897-1898
Zimmern, Nathalie Herman (Secretary, Asst. Curator American Indian Arts and Primitive Cultures, Asst. Curator Primitive and New World Cultures)	1936-1947
Zorach, Margaret B. (Asst. Cataloguer, Cataloguer, Librarian Art Reference Library)	1960-

Gifts or Bequests to

THE BROOKLYN MUSEUM

*are a contribution to the cultural life
of the Borough, the City, and the Nation.
Such gifts may be designated
as Permanent Memorials and are
deductible for tax purposes.*

DESIGNED AND PRINTED BY
PHILIPP VON ZABERN
MAINZ ON RHINE
GERMANY

Type: Walbaum Antiqua. Number of copies: 10,000.